MATCH-POIN  D1584116

This master-work by Hugh Kelsey covers every aspect of match-point bridge from the opening lead in a part-score contract to sacrificing against a grand slam.

It is intended primarily for club players who know the basics of the game and who want to advance rapidly up the ladder. *Match-Point Bridge* will be their bible and an unfailing source of information and guidance of the highest order.

Hugh Kelsey, author of over forty books and twice winner of the Gold Cup, has a world-wide reputation as a top bridge analyst.

by Hugh Kelsey in the *Master Bridge Series*

MATCH-POINT BRIDGE

Hugh Kelsey

VICTOR GOLLANCZ
in association with
PETER CRAWLEY

First published 1970 by Faber & Faber Ltd

This edition first published 1995
in association with Peter Crawley
by Victor Gollancz
An imprint of the Cassell Group
Wellington House, 125 Strand, London WC2R 0BB

A catalogue record for this book
is available from the British Library

ISBN 0 575 04937 5

Printed in Great Britain by
St Edmundsbury Press Ltd, Bury St Edmunds, Suffolk

Contents

9

Contents

Introduction

What Counts at Pairs

THIS book is intended for players who have already had some experience of the match-pointed pairs game. A detailed description of the mechanics of match-point scoring would therefore be out of place, but I propose to touch on the matter briefly. Looking at a familiar subject from a fresh angle can help to identify the targets and bring them into sharper focus.

When you sit down to play in a pairs tournament it is important to know exactly what you are trying to achieve. The winners usually come from a relatively small group of players who have given a lot of thought to the strategy and tactics required in the pairs game. The need for special strategy is dictated entirely by the method of scoring, whereby the results of all pairs who play the same hands are compared and match-points awarded on a flat scale. You receive two match-points for each pair you beat and one for each pair you tie with.

It is this flat scale that makes the difference between pairs and other forms of bridge. It doesn't matter whether you outscore another pair by ten aggregate points or by a thousand; you still get just two match-points for beating them. This peculiarity of the scoring method accounts for all the subtle changes in strategy and tactics that have to be made in the pairs game.

The pairs player's objective on each deal, then, is to outscore the other pairs who are playing the same cards. Note the difference between this and the objective at rubber or team bridge, which is to score as many points as possible on each deal. At pairs you

11

Introduction

are not interested in the number of aggregate points you pile up. You care only about the number of pairs you beat on each hand.

Having defined the objective we are still left with the problem of how to achieve it. The many specialized techniques in both bidding and play will be examined in the main body of the book. In the meantime I would like to remind you of a concept which many players have kept stored away in the attics of their consciousness since S. J. Simon wrote about it years ago. I refer to the concept of absolute par. Simon pointed out that on every competitive hand there are three distinct pars.

A North-South par, representing the maximum score that North and South can obtain playing in their best contract against best defence.

An East-West par, which is the maximum that East and West can obtain in like manner.

And an absolute par, which is the minimum number of points that must be lost by the weaker side.

Ely Culbertson had another name for absolute par. He called it 'the theoretically ideal contract' and defined it as 'the product of the best efforts of both sides'.

Personally I like Simon's term but prefer Culbertson's definition. Absolute par—the product of the best efforts of both sides.

Since Simon's time no writer has given this concept the weight it deserves. I propose to dwell on it at some length, because I believe it is vital for competitors at match-point pairs to appreciate the close relationship that often exists between absolute par and an average match-point score.

Introduction

Consider this very ordinary hand.

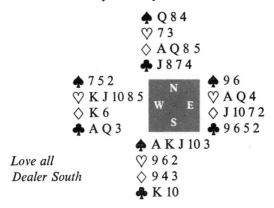

♠ Q 8 4
♡ 7 3
♢ A Q 8 5
♣ J 8 7 4

♠ 7 5 2
♡ K J 10 8 5
♢ K 6
♣ A Q 3

♠ 9 6
♡ A Q 4
♢ J 10 7 2
♣ 9 6 5 2

♠ A K J 10 3
♡ 9 6 2
♢ 9 4 3
♣ K 10

Love all
Dealer South

Against best defence North-South can make eight tricks in spades and East-West can make eight tricks in hearts. Absolute par is reached when West plays in three hearts doubled, giving a score of 100 points to North-South.

Whatever the quality of the field it will be unusual for many pairs to hit par right on the button. There will inevitably be several scores on either side of par, which will mean that one pair or the other has beaten par.

Looking at the deal from the East-West point of view, for instance, it is clear that there are several ways in which they might beat par. If South fails to open the bidding and is again reluctant to come in at the two-level, West might be permitted to play in two hearts, scoring 110. Against timid opponents West might be allowed to play undoubled in three hearts for a score of minus 50. If the defence is loose he might even make three hearts and score 140. Alternatively North or South might contest to three spades, giving East-West 50 or 100 points.

In all these cases the East-West pairs will beat absolute par, and they should all get above-average match-point scores. In a ten-table event the travelling score-sheet for the above deal might look like this.

Introduction

Pair N-S	Pair E-W	Final Contract	Played by	Tricks made	N-S Score +	N-S Score —	Match-points N-S	Match-points E-W
1	11	2 ♠	S	8	110		13	5
2	14	3 ♡x	W	8	100		9	9
3	16	2 ♡	W	9		140	0	18
4	18	3 ♠	S	8		50	4	14
5	20	3 ♠x	S	9	530		18	0
6	12	2 ♠	S	9	140		16	2
7	13	2 ♡	W	8		110	2	16
8	15	2 ♠	S	8	110		13	5
9	17	3 ♡x	W	8	100		9	9
10	19	3 ♡	W	8	50		6	12

Note that the East-West pairs who played in the par contract of three hearts doubled, one down, receive nine match-points out of eighteen—an exact average—as do their North-South opponents. The results that score better than average are those which beat absolute par.

It will not, of course, work out like this on every hand you play. On some deals achieving absolute par may be worth a top score to one pair and a bottom to their opponents. This could come about if the par contract is not easy to reach, or if the par play or par defence is hard to find. The rest of the field might then miss par by a mile.

On most hands, however, absolute par can be roughly equated with an average score, and to achieve a winning session you will have to beat par with fair regularity. It is no good trying for tops, for nobody can produce a top at will. Just try to score on the right side of par for hand after hand after hand.

Suppose we change the vulnerability on the last deal to make it game all. What will be the effect of this? The best theoretical result will now be for East and West to allow North-South to play in two spades. Absolute par will be represented by a score of 110 to North-South instead of 100. The difference is only ten aggregate points, but it will have a marked effect on the score-

Introduction

sheet. The East-West pairs will not now be so frisky, for most players are aware of the danger of conceding 200 for one down doubled on a part-score hand. The travelling score-sheet might look like this.

Pair		Final	Played	Tricks	N-S Score		Match-points	
N-S	E-W	Contract	by	Made	+	—	N-S	E-W
1	11	2 ♠	S	8	110		8	10
2	14	2 ♠	S	8	110		8	10
3	16	2 ♡	W	9		140	0	18
4	18	3 ♠	S	8		100	4	14
5	20	3 ♠x	S	9	730		18	0
6	12	2 ♠	S	9	140		13	5
7	13	2 ♡	W	8		110	2	16
8	15	2 ♠	S	8	110		8	10
9	17	3 ♡x	W	8	200		16	2
10	19	2 ♠	S	9	140		13	5

At love all it was worth only five match-points out of eighteen for East-West to allow their opponents to play in two spades making eight tricks. But at game all this is the par result and is worth ten points, just above average, to East-West. From this it is clear that the vulnerability is a big factor in the contested auction.

In competitive situations, as S. J. Simon pointed out, absolute par represents the pivot of the entire game. This applies with particular force in the pairs game, where reaching absolute par will normally produce a near-average score. It is on these competitive deals that you must aim at beating par regularly.

On the deals where your side has most of the high cards and the opponents do not enter the bidding, your objective is different. Absolute par will now be identical with your own par, and it would be foolish to try to beat that. All you need do is make sure that you do not fall below your own par. This is where constructive bidding comes into its own by helping you to reach the best match-point contract. An opportunity for beating par may arise

Introduction

in the play of the hand when weak defence by the opponents allows you to snatch an overtrick.

It is important to realize that it is impossible to beat absolute par without the help of the opponents. Before you can beat par the opponents must slip up somewhere—must fail to reach *their* par either in bidding, play or defence. That is why a large part of bidding technique should be directed towards making it difficult for opponents to reach their par.

When the opponents have all the strength and you are unable to dredge up a competitive overcall, there is no need to feel too unhappy about allowing the enemy to operate in peace. Part of the time they will operate in your favour, presenting you with an undeserved top by failing to reach their par match-point contract. In defence your main concern will be to avoid falling below par by giving the declarer a present of an overtrick. But if the declarer adopts an inferior line of play you must be quick to seize on any chance of beating par.

Temperament

Pairs is a particularly tense game. A tough session of bridge is always tiring, of course. You may end up with a headache after a session of rubber bridge or a team of four match, but pairs headaches are apt to be bigger and better. This is because a high level of concentration has to be maintained over a period of several hours. There is no chance to relax until the last board has been played.

Other forms of the game are not quite so demanding. The level of interest and concentration tends to vary with the size of the hand being played. Most players wind their concentration up to a peak for game and slam hands and slacken off a little on the part-scores. This is especially the case in defence. The best of players is apt to nod a little when defending against a two-diamond contract which the declarer is bound to make anyway.

At pairs it can be fatal to take it easy in this manner. Every board is of equal importance. The same number of match-points

Introduction

are at stake whether the contract is two diamonds or seven no trumps doubled, and a lapse of concentration can all too easily result in a bottom score.

External disturbances can affect the concentration, but this is not usually a serious problem. Keen players become so absorbed by the game that they can ignore their environment. What you really have to watch out for is what goes on in your own mind. The deadliest assaults on your concentration come from within.

In all fields of endeavour emotion is the arch-enemy of judgement. Bridge is no exception. In match-pointed pairs it is particularly vital to bring to each situation a calm and dispassionate mind—a mind completely devoid of emotion. *Any* kind of emotion is undesirable, whether it be anger at your partner's sloppy defence, indignation over your opponents' rotten bidding, resentment of a wounding remark, irritation at the way a kibitzer sucks his teeth, or despair over the number of zeros on your scorecard. Even elation can be dangerous. A player who tackles the next hand while mentally hugging himself over a good result is very likely to land himself with a poor score to cancel out the good one. If you have done something clever by all means have a little silent gloat in between boards (you are not, I trust, so discourteous as to gloat out loud). But as soon as you reach for your cards on the next deal you had better banish all thoughts of the good result and concentrate your attention on the new hand.

The pairs player must learn, as Kipling puts it, 'to meet with triumph and disaster and treat those two impostors just the same'. You may find this easy enough where triumph is concerned, but disaster can be very hard to bear. It is not easy to keep your poise when you suffer a calamity through no fault of your own.

Introduction

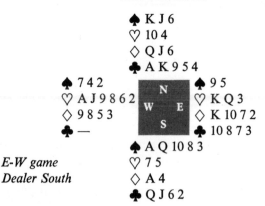

```
                    ♠ K J 6
                    ♡ 10 4
                    ◇ Q J 6
                    ♣ A K 9 5 4
        ♠ 7 4 2          N          ♠ 9 5
        ♡ A J 9 8 6 2   W   E      ♡ K Q 3
        ◇ 9 8 5 3                   ◇ K 10 7 2
        ♣ —              S          ♣ 10 8 7 3
                    ♠ A Q 10 8 3
E-W game            ♡ 7 5
Dealer South        ◇ A 4
                    ♣ Q J 6 2
```

You reach the normal contract of four spades and West makes the far from normal lead of the heart two. East wins with the queen, gives his partner a club ruff, and regains the lead with the heart king to give West another club ruff. One down!

What could be more aggravating? On a double-dummy basis the par contract is five clubs, but nobody will play there. They will all be in four spades, and the par defence is so obscure that no other East-West pair may find it. Some declarers will make ten tricks, some eleven, and a good number will be allowed to make twelve. The best you can hope for is that someone will share the bottom spot with you. Where is the justice in this? You have performed as well as any other North-South pair, and yet you get a bottom while others get a top.

You just have to shrug your shoulders and accept an occasional fix like this, consoling yourself with the reflection that an un-merited zero is often balanced by an unmerited top in the same session.

The most agonizing deals are those on which you receive a bottom and realize at the same time that a top was there for the taking. The following hand was responsible for a few extra milli-metres of wear on East's dentures.

Introduction

```
                    ♠ K 8 5
Game all            ♡ 10 6 5
Dealer South        ◇ K 9 4 3
                    ♣ A 10 2
South    North                    ♠ 7 6 4 2
1 NT     3 NT                     ♡ A Q 9 4 3
                                  ◇ Q 7
                                  ♣ K 8
```

North and South were playing a variable no-trump opening, and at this vulnerability the range was 15–17 points.

West led the queen of spades, South won with the ace and ran the queen of clubs to East's king. Since South was marked with the king of hearts, East gave no thought to a switch but simply returned his partner's suit. This defence was not a success, for the other two hands were as shown below.

```
          ♠ Q J 9 3
          ♡ K 8 2
          ◇ J 10 6 2
          ♣ 6 5

                    ♠ A 10
                    ♡ J 7
                    ◇ A 8 5
                    ♣ Q J 9 7 4 3
```

'Sorry,' said South, after raking in his nine tricks. 'I forgot we were vulnerable.'

The apology was little comfort to East and West, who were the unwilling victims of South's forgetfulness.

When two or three such boards come in quick succession the most phlegmatic of players is hard-pressed to keep calm. It is only too easy to give in to the feeling that you are not destined to win the session, and once you do that you are lost.

It is after a series of disastrous boards that the true moral fibre of a pair makes itself known. I remember once kibitzing at a Howell tournament and seeing a certain South player get a foul

19

Introduction

result by going two down vulnerable in a one no trump contract. North calmly entered the score on the sheet, and he and South sat quiet and pensive while awaiting the call to move. East and West, however, thought they might have defeated the contract by three tricks, and tempers flared as what began as a difference of opinion on suit preference developed into a slanging match.

Eventually South said mildly: 'You know, this is the wrong way round—the pair who got the top having an argument and the pair who got the bottom not saying a word.'

The incongruity of the situation appealed to East and West and they burst out laughing. But it is significant that it was North and South who went on to win the tournament.

The right mental attitude is well worth acquiring. Players who are naturally serene and even-tempered have a great advantage at the pairs game. Those who are not must practise to achieve serenity. This can be done by the exercise of rigid self-discipline, and it *must* be done if you are to make the most of your technical ability.

PART ONE

Fundamentals

1

Bidding

Controlled Aggression

> Twice armed is he who knows his cause is just,
> But thrice armed he who gets his blow in fust.
>
> ANON.

Do you and your partner normally play more hands than your opponents? Perhaps it is a question that has never occurred to you, but the answer is significant. For if you examine the results of a pairs session you will find, nine times out of ten, that the winners played more hands than their opponents.

Good players are not content to win the declaration only when they hold the balance of power. They steal some of their opponents' hands as well. They do this with their eyes wide open, as part of a deliberate policy. And when they do it they usually achieve a good result, whether they are doubled or not.

Aggressive bidding is the cornerstone of their game, and this is the basis of all success at pairs.

What about system? My own preference is for Acol, the system on which I cut my teeth. The full use of limit bids and the minimum number of forcing sequences make it an ideal system for pairs, where part-scores are every bit as important as games and slams. But this is not a book about systems and it is clearly not necessary to play Acol to be a good pairs player. Use any system you like, provided that you cultivate an aggressive style. It is important to be able to open light on distributional hands and to be able to intervene freely, getting into the bidding whenever

23

Fundamentals

there may be an advantage and out again before you get out of your depth.

The First Blow

Aggression begins with the opening bid, and the most aggressive one-level opening is the bid of one no trump. This defines strength and distribution within narrow limits and thus keeps your partner in comfort while frequently putting your opponents on the spot. By pre-empting the one-level you compel opponents either to stay out of the auction or to start their dialogue at the two-level. And there may be danger for them in either course.

More and more players all over the world are adopting the weak no trump for pairs play. One reason is the frequency of occurrence. Players wish to make use of this aggressive, semi-pre-emptive opening as often as possible. It is worth noting that 9·7 per cent of all the bridge hands you hold are suitable for a weak (12–14 point) no trump, whereas only 4·9 per cent qualify for a strong (15–17 point) no trump. Thus on the grounds of frequency alone the weak no trump is a vastly superior weapon for match-point pairs.

The argument is valid whatever the vulnerability. Some bottoms will inevitably come your way when your weak no trump is doubled and goes for 500 or 800. (Oddly enough, the last 1100 I can remember from the double of an opening no trump happened five years ago—and then it was a strong no trump that bought it.) But the weak no trump will earn you a number of small victories over par for every toss it takes, and in pairs, remember, it is the frequency of success that determines the usefulness of a bid, not the number of points it gains or loses.

When it comes to suit bids, any inhibitions about point-count requirements for opening the bidding can act like a millstone round your neck. The pairs player simply cannot afford to keep quiet when he has a distributional hand with good playing strength.

Bidding

(a)	♠ A 10 9 5 2	(b)	♠ K J 10 7 6 3
	♡ A 9 8 4 2		♡ 4
	◇ 10 5		◇ A 7 5 4
	♣ 6		♣ 8 3

Neither of the above hands comes up to the standard laid down for opening bids in any books on bidding. Yet I suggest that few successful pairs players would fail to open on them in any position and at any vulnerability.

Hand (a) is the type on which you may be able to make four in a major while the opponents can make three no trumps. If you pass originally the bidding may be at three no trumps when next it comes round and you will be lost.

On (b) you might have a cheap save against an opposing heart game. Par on the hand could be four spades doubled, one off, but if you pass originally your next chance to bid may come at the four-level. Many players would choose to open hand (b) with a weak two bid in spades or with a Multi two diamonds, but if you do not play such methods there is no need to keep silent. Provided that Partner is trained to respect your sign-off bids, there is little risk in opening one spade on the hand.

Boss Suit

Note that in both the above examples the spade suit is held. On border-line hands this plays a big part in determining whether to open the bidding. Neither of the above hands would be worth opening if the long suits were minors, and both would be doubtful cases if only hearts were held.

Next to one no trump, one spade is the most pre-emptive one-level bid you can make. The opponents have to go to the two-level to mention their suit, and if partner can raise your spades they may be reluctant to offer their necks to the chopper at the three-level.

In competitive situations the side that possesses the spade suit enjoys an overwhelming advantage, and for this reason a large group of expert players believe that it is highly desirable to stake an early claim to the spade suit whether you possess it or not.

The safe time to do this is when you are third in hand after two passes. Sub-minimum openings on balanced hands can have a valuable obstructive effect and can also be useful in indicating a safe lead.

(a) ♠ A Q 6	(b) ♠ Q J 4 3	(c) ♠ K J 10
♡ 9 5	♡ J 7	♡ K 6 4
◇ K 9 6 2	◇ A J 5 3 2	◇ 9 8 3
♣ Q 6 5 2	♣ Q 8	♣ A 8 5 4

A third hand opening of one spade on any of the above hands is unlikely to come to much harm, since you are prepared to pass any response your partner may make. Third hand bids on three-card suits can be real par-beaters on occasion, and the suit does not have to be spades.

(d) ♠ J 7 6 4	(e) ♠ 6 5	(f) ♠ 7 6 4 2
♡ A J 9	♡ K Q 3	♡ 9 7
◇ K J 6 2	◇ K Q 4 3	◇ A K Q
♣ 10 5	♣ J 8 4 2	♣ 10 8 7 3

On (d) and (e) a one heart opening may steal the opponents' suit, while on (f) a one diamond opening could keep the opponents out of a cinch three no trumps.

In fourth position after three passes, you are not mainly concerned with obstruction, of course. The purpose of opening is to obtain a plus score of some sort, but in this position as well the power of the major suits, especially spades, makes itself felt. Sub-minimum hands should be opened only if you have the spade suit, or at least something in both majors.

(a) ♠ A Q 10 7 5	(b) ♠ J 10 5 4	(c) ♠ K Q J 7 6 2
♡ K J 3	♡ K Q 9 8 4	♡ 8
◇ 10 9 4	◇ A 5 2	◇ K 10 7
♣ 6 2	♣ 7	♣ 9 8 3

Bidding

If you open one spade on (*a*) and (*c*) and one heart on (*b*) there is a good chance that you will be able to outbid the opponents and obtain a part-score.

Minor suit hands, however, are often passed out in fourth position, even when the hand is full strength and would be opened in any other seat.

(*d*) ♠ 4 2	(*e*) ♠ 7
♡ J 6	♡ 10 9 6
◇ K J 8 7 6 4	◇ A 8 7 5
♣ A K 3	♣ A K J 6 2

No one could say you haven't an opening on either of the above hands, but I believe the winning policy at pairs is to throw them in if you are fourth in hand. You will seldom score a zero by passing out such hands, but if you open and find that the enemy can outbid you in the majors you will get few match-points.

Raising Partner's Suit

In the aggressive modern style players tend to raise partner's suit, particularly a major suit, on the sketchiest of values. Not only does this have an obstructive effect, but it is actually safer to show a modicum of strength at the earliest opportunity rather than back into the auction at a later stage or rely upon partner to reopen.

The raise is made on the same values whether an opponent makes an intervening bid or not. The ancient myth of the 'free raise' showing extra values has long since been exploded.

(*a*) ♠ K 6 5 4 2	(*b*) ♠ A 8 6	(*c*) ♠ 8 6 5 3
♡ 8 5	♡ 7 6 2	♡ 4
◇ 6 4 3	◇ Q 9 4	◇ 10 7 4 2
♣ 9 8 5	♣ 7 5 4 3	♣ K 9 8 5

On (*a*) and (*c*) you should raise partner's one spade opening to two, whether second hand puts in an overcall of two hearts or

Fundamentals

not. With (*b*) you will respond one no trump if second hand is silent, but over two hearts you should compete with two spades. Your partner may not be able to make two spades in any of these cases, but remember that at pairs the object of bidding is not to arrive at makeable contracts. It is to beat par. Going one down in two spades may give you an excellent score.

Similar light raises can be given in the other suits.

(*d*) ♠ 7
   ♡ Q 6 5 4
   ◇ Q 10 5 2
   ♣ 9 7 6 3

(*e*) ♠ J 9 8 6
   ♡ 3
   ◇ 10 9 5
   ♣ K 8 7 4 2

(*f*) ♠ K 7 4
   ♡ 9 2
   ◇ Q 6 4 2
   ♣ 8 7 6 2

On each of the above hands you should pass if partner bids your short suit, but raise any other suit bid to two.

Match-Point Contracts

Obstructive tactics will be covered more fully in later chapters. In the meantime let us turn our attention to the effect of match-point scoring on constructive bidding.

In an uncontested auction you are concerned with reaching par rather than beating it. Nevertheless, some risks must be taken because of the extra premium for major suit and no trump contracts.

When your side has the balance of power most of the pairs playing your way will register plus scores, and in order to do well you will need to aim for the largest possible plus score. For this reason you should sometimes elect to play in a risky no trump or major suit contract rather than a safe minor suit spot.

This applies particularly at the game level. At pairs it can never be right to play in five of a minor suit when there is any playable alternative.

Bidding

♠ A Q 10	
♡ 6 4	
◊ A Q 8 4	*Love all*
♣ A J 10 3	*Dealer North*

	North	South
♠ K J 7 3	1 ◊	1 ♠
♡ 8	3 ♠	4 ♠
◊ K 10 7 6 3 2		
♣ 7 5		

The above bidding is typical of the pairs game. Five diamonds is the safest game contract, but this would score only 400. The same eleven tricks are likely to be available in spades if the suit breaks no worse than 4–2. This gives a score of 450, therefore four spades is the superior match-point contract. Even if the opponents can obtain a diamond ruff a score of 420 will still beat those who play in diamonds.

More often the choice is between a minor suit game and three no trumps, and the experienced pairs player chooses the nine-trick game whenever there appears to be a play for it.

♠ 7	
♡ 4	
◊ A K 10 8 7 6 4 3	*Game all*
♣ Q 6 2	*Dealer South*

	South	North
♠ A J 6 3	1 ♣	1 ◊
♡ K 9 5	1 NT	3 NT
◊ Q 5		
♣ A J 8 7		

North's raise to three no trumps on a hand containing two unbid singletons may look extreme, but a minimum of ten tricks are available at no trumps and this will outscore those who play in five diamonds. In a rubber or team game North's second bid would of course be five diamonds, but at pairs this is not good enough. If by some miscalculation North found himself beyond the three no trump level, he should bid six diamonds rather than five. The odds are against the slam making, but it is better to go down fighting than to play in five diamonds for what is sure to be a poor score.

This does not mean that you should *never* play in five of a minor. Hands do turn up where the only possible game is in a minor suit. The players who make it a fixed rule never to rest in five of a minor then find themselves going one down in a hopeless slam for a bottom score.

Game all. Dealer East

	West	North	East	South
♠ A 7			1♡	2♣
♡ A J 5 3				
◇ —	2♡	3♣	—	?
♣ A 10 8 6 5 4 3				

At this point South's only sensible bid is five clubs. Anything less would be cowardly, six would be greedy, while three no trumps would be a wild gamble.

Often a no trump game should be chosen in preference to four of a major.

	Love all	
♠ A K Q 10 6 3	*Dealer North*	
♡ 7 6 4		
◇ Q 2	North	South
♣ 9 7	1 NT	?

When partner opens a weak no trump there are three reasons for preferring a raise to three no trumps to a bid of four spades. First, it is better to have the lead coming up to your partner's hand. Second, nine tricks may be the limit in any denomination, and third, even if four spades is a make the same number of tricks may be available in no trumps.

The first objection might be overcome by the use of a transfer bid, but the other two are weighty enough to make three no trumps the better match-point bid. It could be wrong, of course. It is easy enough to construct a hand for partner on which four spades will make while three no trumps goes down or is held to nine tricks. But such cases will be in the minority, and at pairs one should always go for the contract that offers the greater probability of a good score.

When you have a solid suit to run, whether it be major or minor, three no trumps will often be the best spot. If you have doubts about the texture of your suit, on the other hand, the suit contract should be chosen.

When you have a four-four fit in a major suit the hand will normally play at least one trick better in the suit contract. Four of a major scores better than three no trumps, and eleven tricks in the major beats ten in no trumps, so this is an occasion to prefer the major suit game.

♠ A 8 6 5		
♡ K J 5 2	*Game all*	
◇ K 8	*Dealer North*	
♣ K 7 4	*North*	*South*
	1 NT	2 ♣
♠ J 7 4 2	2 ♡	2 NT
♡ Q 10	4 ♠	—
◇ A 7 6 4		
♣ A 3 2		

The Stayman convention may occasionally give away too much information to the enemy, but its usefulness in locating major suits outweighs the disadvantage, even at pairs. Note that North, holding a maximum hand and assured of a fit, takes the pressure off his partner by going straight to game in his second major.

The contract of four spades depends on little more than the normal 3–2 trump break, whereas a good deal of luck would be needed to make even nine tricks at no trumps.

The decision is closer when your major suit is divided 5–3, 5–2, or even 4–3. The major suit game should usually be preferred when obvious ruffing values are present, and also when the hands are rich in top controls but short of intermediate stuffing. No hard and fast rules can be laid down, however. Three no trumps has the great advantage of being the cheapest game bid available and also the game most often allowed to make when it should be defeated.

Fundamentals

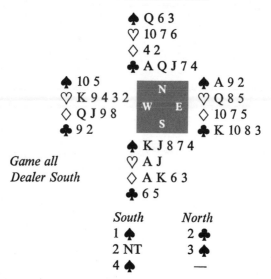

```
              ♠ Q 6 3
              ♡ 10 7 6
              ◇ 4 2
              ♣ A Q J 7 4
♠ 10 5                        ♠ A 9 2
♡ K 9 4 3 2      N           ♡ Q 8 5
◇ Q J 9 8    W     E         ◇ 10 7 5
♣ 9 2           S            ♣ K 10 8 3
              ♠ K J 8 7 4
              ♡ A J
              ◇ A K 6 3
              ♣ 6 5
```

Game all
Dealer South

South	North
1 ♠	2 ♣
2 NT	3 ♠
4 ♠	—

The normal match-point bidding is as shown above, but we all know players who would take a flying leap at three no trumps after North's two club bid. On this occasion they might achieve a top score because, although both three no trumps and four spades can be defeated, the no trump game is likely to make in practice. It requires almost a double-dummy defence to beat three no trumps, but four spades has little chance on normal defence.

Nevertheless, four spades is the contract you would wish to be in if you could see only the North and South hands, and 420 will be a top score if you get away with it. And if you go down you will still get a few match-points for you will be in good company.

Close Games

This is as good a time as any to examine the question of border-line game hands. Should the game be bid or not?

In an uncontested auction where the bidding will follow a similar course at most tables, experienced players try to go with

32

the field in making the final decision. By making the bid which most of the other players will make they assure themselves of some match-points on the board. Suppose the top is ten on each board. Following the field will result in a score of about seven if the decision is the right one and about three if it is wrong. Being out of step with the others will give you perhaps a nine or a one. The good player does not like to gamble on close bidding decisions. A few threes on his score card he can stand, but ones are another matter. He therefore chooses to play down the middle on such boards, relying on superior judgement on the competitive hands to pull his score above average.

This means that the game should normally be bid, for most players are healthily aggressive in their bidding habits and a fifty-fifty game will be bid more often than not. In the bidding it is very hard to estimate whether a game will have a fifty-fifty chance anyway. If there appears to be any reasonable chance of success you should wish to be in game.

What you must guard against is overbidding your values in an attempt to reach close games. Do not try to make your partner's decisions for him. Give him a chance to stop below game if he has a minimum hand. Stretching or pressing can result only in poor match-point scores.

Part-Scores

The choice of denomination at the part-score level is governed by the same general considerations as at the game level. When the enemy do not contest the bidding the hand belongs to you, and your aim is still to obtain the highest possible plus score. However, you should be slightly more safety-conscious in choosing your part-score contract. It is probable that some pairs will get too high and register a minus score on the board, and any plus score is likely to earn a few match-points. There is thus not quite the same urgency to play in a high-scoring denomination, and minor suit contracts are accepted with less reluctance than at the game level.

Fundamentals

A playable major suit should normally be preferred to no trumps, since the chances are that the hand will play one trick better in the suit.

♠ J 8 7 3	*Love all*
♡ J 5	*Dealer North*
◇ 10 9 5	North South
♣ A 9 6 4	1 ♠ 2 ♠
	2 NT ?

South's proper rebid is of course three spades. You may say this is obvious, but I have seen players pass two no trumps on this hand in the belief that they were playing a clever match-point game. I have even seen one raise to three no trumps!

Considerations of safety should not deter you from taking a reasonable risk in giving preference to a major suit.

♠ A J 7 5	*Game all*
♡ J 7	*Dealer North*
◇ Q 6 5	North South
♣ 8 5 4 3	1 ♡ 1 ♠
	2 ◇ ?

At other forms of bridge a pass would be best, but at pairs you should give false preference to two hearts in the hope of achieving a larger plus score.

There is a subtle difference in the next example.

♠ A 10 8 5 4	
♡ 9 4	North South
◇ 8 7 3	1 ♡ 1 ♠
♣ K 10 9	2 ♣ ?

Since your partner's suits are not touching there is a greater risk that he has only four hearts (a 1–4–4–4 hand) and you should therefore pass.

On some hands a 4–3 major suit fit will prove a better spot than either a 4–4 minor or no trumps.

Bidding

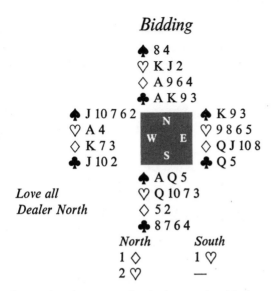

♠ 8 4
♡ K J 2
◇ A 9 6 4
♣ A K 9 3

♠ J 10 7 6 2
♡ A 4
◇ K 7 3
♣ J 10 2

♠ K 9 3
♡ 9 8 6 5
◇ Q J 10 8
♣ Q 5

♠ A Q 5
♡ Q 10 7 3
◇ 5 2
♣ 8 7 6 4

Love all
Dealer North

North	South
1 ◇	1 ♡
2 ♡	—

Those who choose to play in hearts should share the top score of 140. Those who play in clubs will not do badly, making ten tricks for a score of 130. But anyone who plays in no trumps is likely to find that normal defence holds him to eight tricks, and 120 will be a poor result.

In choosing between a minor suit and no trumps it must be remembered that the hand will need to play two tricks better in the minor suit to make the latter the proper match-point contract. It is usually right to prefer the no trump contract when there will be any reasonable play for it.

♠ 6 5
♡ J 8 5
◇ A Q 8 7 4 2
♣ 10 3

Game all
Dealer South

♠ Q J 8
♡ K 4
◇ K 9 6 3
♣ A Q 7 5

South	North
1 ♣	1 ◇
?	

Fundamentals

South's match-point rebid is one no trumps. There are eight sure tricks in no trumps, and the score of 120 is unlikely to be beaten by those who play in diamonds.

As a general rule, when you have a long suit to run the no trump contract will probably be superior. It is when your suit is broken that you should give serious consideration to playing in the minor.

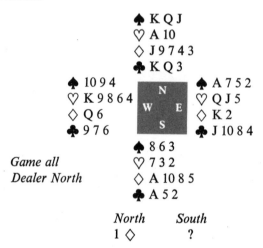

```
              ♠ K Q J
              ♡ A 10
              ◇ J 9 7 4 3
              ♣ K Q 3
  ♠ 10 9 4              ♠ A 7 5 2
  ♡ K 9 8 6 4           ♡ Q J 5
  ◇ Q 6                 ◇ K 2
  ♣ 9 7 6               ♣ J 10 8 4
              ♠ 8 6 3
Game all      ♡ 7 3 2
Dealer North  ◇ A 10 8 5
              ♣ A 5 2
```

North	South
1 ◇	?

If no trumps is the right spot it would be better for the no trump bid to come from North, so I would choose a raise to two diamonds on the South hand in spite of the lack of ruffing values.

Now look at North's problem when his partner raises to two diamonds. His hand is on the border-line for a rebid of two no trumps, but the poor quality of his diamonds should influence him to pass.

Interchange North's spade and diamond honours and the position is very different.

```
              ♠ J 9 7
              ♡ A 10
              ◇ K Q J 4 3
              ♣ K Q 3
```

Bidding

If partner raises your diamond bid to two the above hand is certainly worth two no trumps, for there is now an excellent chance of being able to run the diamond suit without loss. Whether partner raises to three no trumps, passes, or signs off in three diamonds, you should be in a good match-point contract.

On Bidding Close Slams

Punch's advice to those about to marry is appropriate—don't.

Pursuing the policy of playing down the middle, you will not of course want to miss a slam that most of the other pairs are in. But it definitely does not pay to strain after border-line slams at match-point pairs. The wisest course is to bid those slams which are obvious to you and let the others go.

When chalking up your 680 it should not worry you to see that a couple of geniuses have scored 1,430 on the board. No partnership is good enough to bid all the close slams that come their way. Your 680 will be in good company and your match-point score will not be much below average. Going down in a close slam, however, would earn you something very like a zero.

When the slam is obvious to you the choice of suits is unlikely to be a problem. Any slam you make should give you a good score, so choose the safest denomination. It is worth bearing in mind, however, that the safest denomination might well be no trumps. A no trump slam may be better able to withstand a bad break in any particular suit, and there is also no risk of an adverse ruff. The rock-crusher grand slams, where you have every suit stopped and fifteen tricks on top, should naturally be played in no trumps.

2

Dummy Play

MODIFIED techniques for the pairs game are not confined to the bidding; the play of the hand also calls for a different approach. This does not mean that specialized match-point techniques will be required on every deal. Most hands should be played in exactly the same manner whether the game is pairs or rubber bridge. The quirks of match-point scoring are such, however, that a shift of emphasis is necessary. The tendency is away from safety. In an effort to obtain the largest possible plus score, players take risks which would be unthinkable at rubber bridge.

Under aggregate scoring, bidding and play are separate phases of the game with no close relationship between them. The object of bidding is to reach the best contract, but when dummy goes down you can forget the bidding and concentrate on the play. Whether the contract is good or bad, you must give yourself the best chance of making it. Overtricks and undertricks are normally of very minor significance. It is the making of the contract that is all-important.

The more closely integrated relationship between bidding and play in the pairs game is not always fully understood. Good match-point bidding should arrive at the best-scoring (not necessarily the best or the safest) contract, but nobody can hope to achieve this all the time. Your approach to the play must vary according to how well you have succeeded in the bidding. Certain match-point decisions will have been taken during the course of the bidding and it is important to back up these decisions, whether they appear to be right or wrong, in the play of the hand. The proper attitude is to regard the play as an extension of the bidding and aim for consistency. There is no surer way of getting a bottom score than adopting a line of play that is inconsistent with your bidding.

When dummy goes down on the table your first task is to evaluate your contract, comparing it with the contracts likely to be reached at the other tables. You must decide, in other words, whether or not you have reached your bidding par. You will expect to be in the correct match-point contract most of the time, but inevitably there will be some deals on which you judge that you have fallen below par in the bidding.

These are the deals on which special match-point recovery techniques will be required in the play of the hand. They should not comprise more than 20 per cent of all the hands you play, and this sort of deal is allotted space in this book out of propor- tion to its frequency of occurrence.

On some occasions you will have underbid and apparently missed an easy game, on others you will have bid too strongly and landed in a seemingly impossible contract. Or perhaps you will be at the right level but in what appears to be an inferior denomi- nation.

In such cases you are doomed to a very poor match-point score if your estimate of par is correct. The only hope of scoring well lies in keeping faith with your bidding. However unlikely it may appear, you must assume that on this particular deal it is your estimate of par and not your bidding that is at fault. You must therefore revise your estimate of par. When you have underbid, make sure of your plus score and assume that bad breaks will defeat the normal game. When you have overbid, try to envisage a lie of the cards favourable enough to enable you to make your

Fundamentals

contract. If that is clearly impossible, assume that the normal contract will also be defeated on natural play and go against the odds to try for an average board. If you are in the wrong denomination, take whatever chances are needed to enable you to outscore the declarers in the normal contract. In the play of the cards you have to adopt the role of fairy godmother and make your bidding come true.

In the majority of hands you expect to be in the normal matchpoint contract and the play should then present no great problems. You will just play to make as many tricks as are consistent with reasonable safety. By playing down the middle you are assured of an above-average score, for there will be some pairs who fail to reach, or overshoot, the par contract.

But what is reasonable safety? What risks should be taken in the quest for overtricks, and when should you play safe?

Many players assume that safety play can never be right in the pairs game, but there are certain well-defined situations in which it is perfectly proper. The most obvious occasion is when you have a chance of making a doubled contract. Just making will always produce a good score, so play it as safe as you can. When you have reached a good distributional game contract which you judge that few of the other pairs will reach, that is another good moment to forget about overtricks and utilize any safety play that is available.

If everyone is in the par contract, you will in theory come out even by taking a fifty-fifty chance for an overtrick. Half the time you will make your overtrick for a top, and half the time you will go down and get a bottom. But you can seldom be sure that everyone will be in the par contract. Usually some pairs will miss it, in which case just making your contract will score above average. In such circumstances a fifty-fifty shot is not good enough, since you stand to lose more than you can gain. Odds of six to four on would perhaps be acceptable, but it is difficult to generalize about this. You must decide each case on its merits, bearing always in mind your sole objective of outscoring as many pairs as possible.

Dummy Play

♠ 9 7 6 3
♡ K 5
♢ A 8 6 5
♣ K J 7

Game all
Dealer South

South	North
1 ♣	1 ♢
1 ♠	4 ♠

♠ A 8 4 2
♡ A 9 4
♢ 3
♣ A Q 10 6 2

West leads the queen of diamonds against your four spade contract. How do you plan the play?

You are in the par contract and it is likely that most of the other pairs will also reach it. It only remains to decide how many tricks will suffice for a good score.

At aggregate or i.m.p. scoring you would look for the safest way of making the contract, and a good safety play is available to guard against a 4–1 trump break. Cash the ace of trumps and then play on clubs, allowing the opponents to make three trumps but no more tricks.

At pairs you cannot afford this safety play, since eleven tricks may be made when the trumps break 3–2. The 3–2 break has a frequency of 68 per cent against 28 per cent for the 4–1 break. The odds are good enough to justify the risk of defeat, so you set your target at eleven tricks.

The best line is to duck a trump at trick two, ruff the diamond return, and cash the ace of spades. If both opponents follow, you will switch to clubs and rake in your eleven tricks.

Had either opponent doubled the final contract, however, there would be two good reasons for thinking again. Not only would there be a strong indication of a bad break in trumps, but there would be no need to strive for overtricks to ensure a good score. The double should therefore persuade you to make the safety play of the ace of spades at trick two.

Fundamentals

♠ 8 7 3
♡ 7 4 3
◇ A Q 10 8 2
♣ 6 5

Love all
Dealer South

South	North

♠ A Q J 10   2 ♣   2 ◇
♡ A K 8   3 NT   6 NT
◇ K J 6
♣ A K 9

West leads the queen of clubs against your small slam. How should you play?

Again you are in the best contract and the rest of the field will be right there with you. This time you have twelve certain tricks and no question of safety is involved. There is the possibility of an overtrick when East has the king of spades, however, and this simple little hand is included just to illustrate the need for care in giving yourself the best chance of making the overtrick.

There will be no problem if East's king is only once guarded, nor if it is twice guarded unless East also has all five outstanding diamonds. But if East has three or more small spades with the king you will need to enter dummy three times in order to finesse. The three entries you require may be available if you handle the diamond suit correctly.

You should lead the king of diamonds at trick two and, if West follows, overtake with dummy's ace. After a successful spade finesse you can repeat the manœuvre with the knave of diamonds. If East followed to the first round and West follows now, it will be safe to overtake once more in dummy, thus gaining the three entries you may need.

Care must be taken not to allow the urge for overtricks to oust common sense and become an obsession. Nothing should persuade you to abandon the best odds in cases like the following.

Dummy Play

♠ Q J 7
♡ K 6 2
◇ A K J 10
♣ A 9 5

East-West game
Dealer South

South	North
4 ♡	6 ♡

♠ —
♡ A Q J 9 8 7 5 3
◇ 7 5
♣ 8 4 3

West leads the king of clubs against your six heart contract. How should you play?

This time your contract is not so good. On the whole it is as well to stay out of this kind of slam at match-point pairs. Certainly it will not be bid at a number of tables and you will get a poor score if you go down.

The best chance of making twelve tricks is to win the first trick, draw trumps in your hand, then cash ace and king of diamonds and take a ruffing finesse against the queen. This line succeeds whenever East has the queen of diamonds and also when West has the queen singleton or doubleton. In the latter event you will make thirteen tricks, of course, and your total chance of success is about 55 per cent.

The direct finesse gives you only a 50 per cent chance, but some players might argue that this is the better pairs play since if it succeeds you will always make an overtrick. Thirteen tricks are better than twelve, they will claim, therefore the direct finesse should be risked.

The argument sounds plausible, but it is quite fallacious. The point is that if West has the queen of diamonds nobody at all will make twelve tricks. They will be making either eleven or thirteen, and so in this case the overtrick will be completely useless to you. There is nothing but a straight issue between success and failure on this hand, and you should therefore take the best chance of making the contract.

Fundamentals

♠ Q 4	
♡ Q 6	
◇ A K 10 9 3	*Game all*
♣ A 7 6 3	*Dealer South*

	South	North
♠ A K 7	1 ♡	2 ◇
♡ A J 10 9 5	3 NT	6 NT
◇ Q 2		
♣ K 10 4		

West leads the five of spades and you win on the table with the queen. You run the queen of hearts successfully and play a second heart to your nine, West following small. How should you continue?

Twelve tricks are easy and the only problem is to find the best play for an overtrick. Many players would cash the ace of hearts at this stage. If the king did not drop they would be reluctant to settle for twelve tricks and would play off the top diamonds. This play is not safe, however, for East could have both red suits stopped.

It is unlikely that the king of hearts will drop anyway. With fewer than four hearts East would surely have covered dummy's queen. The sensible course is to retain the ace of hearts in your hand and try the diamonds first.

There are two lines of play which are almost equally good. You might cash the queen of diamonds and finesse the nine on the second round, or alternatively you could play off the top honours.

The latter method has a slight edge, for if the knave does not come down and East shows out you can then revert to hearts just in case the king is dropping. If East proves to have the guarded knave of diamonds, of course, you will have to concede a diamond and settle for twelve tricks.

Dummy Play

♠ 5
♡ 7 6 3
◇ A Q 9 7 5 4   *East-West game*
♣ J 8 4   *Dealer South*

                                 South   *North*

♠ J 10 8 3   1 ♡   2 ♡
♡ A K Q 4
◇ K 6 3
♣ Q 2

Against your two heart contract West leads the king of spades and then switches to the ten of trumps. How should you plan the play?

If trumps break evenly it may be possible to make no fewer than eleven tricks here—four trumps, a spade ruff and six diamonds. But there is danger in going for spade ruffs. The odds are against an even break in trumps, and if they break 4–2 you will probably go down in your contract. Even if you manage to ruff two spades in dummy you will have your work cut out to collect eight tricks.

Doing a proper job of evaluating your contract should convince you that there is no need to take any risks on this hand. Your partner's slightly unorthodox raise has placed you in an extremely good match-point contract. Those who play in diamonds will make ten tricks at the most, while anyone playing in no trumps is unlikely to be allowed to score more than 120. If you make just nine tricks in hearts your score of 140 will be good enough to beat the pairs playing in diamonds or no trumps.

Nine tricks is a comfortable target which is always within reach if the trumps break no worse than 4–2. Just duck the first trump trick. The opponents can then take their two club tricks, but that is all.

Fundamentals

♠ 8 3
♡ J
◇ J 6 5 4 2
♣ A 9 8 7 3

North-South game
Dealer West

	West	North	East	South
♠ A K Q 10 4	3 ♡	—	—	Dbl
♡ 9 6 4	—	4 ♣	—	4 ♠
◇ A Q 9	All pass			
♣ K 10				

Against your four spade contract West leads the ace of hearts and then switches to the nine of spades. How do you plan the play?

This is a hand I played some years ago in a congress pairs final. It is not one of my successes, and I would not be exposing it to the light of day were there not a moral in the tale.

At trick three I led the queen of diamonds from hand. This is not altogether a bad idea, for there is some point in trying to establish the diamond suit while hearts are still controlled by dummy's remaining trump. The play certainly offers the best chance of making eleven tricks.

Where I slipped up was in my evaluation of the contract. I should have realized that four spades was a pretty good contract to be in, that a number of pairs would fail to reach game, and that just making the contract would therefore give me a good enough score. On this hand the sensible thing to do is to forget about overtricks and concentrate on making a safe ten tricks.

The best play is to ruff a heart in dummy and return to hand with the king of clubs in order to draw trumps. With trumps breaking no worse than 4–2 declarer can then concede a diamond and claim ten tricks.

My punishment for misplaying the hand was swift and savage, for the full deal was as follows.

Dummy Play

```
                    ♠ 8 3
                    ♡ J
                    ◇ J 6 5 4 2
                    ♣ A 9 8 7 3
     ♠ 9 6 2                        ♠ J 7 5
     ♡ A K Q 10 8 2                 ♡ 7 5 3
     ◇ 10 8 7 3                     ◇ K
     ♣ —                           ♣ Q J 6 5 4 2
                    ♠ A K Q 10 4
                    ♡ 9 6 4
                    ◇ A Q 9
                    ♣ K 10
```

When the smoke cleared away I was left with just seven tricks, a bottom score, and a partner who, to his credit, was amused rather than homicidal.

On the opening heart lead and trump switch South can make no fewer than twelve tricks if he ruffs a heart and leads a diamond from dummy. That is double-dummy play, of course, since clubs would normally be the safer suit with which to return to hand. As the cards lie West can ruff the king of clubs and cash another heart, but the declarer will find sufficient compensation in the fall of the king of diamonds and will still come to ten tricks.

Morbid curiosity prompted me to hunt out the travelling scoresheet on the following day. I found that a few North-South pairs had defended against heart contracts, scoring from 50 to 500 points, but that most had played in two or three spades, some making and some going down. My worst fears were realized when I saw that nobody else played in game. My greed for an overtrick had converted a top into a bottom.

The last few hands have all warned against straining too hard after overtricks, but there will be many occasions when you will be justified in taking some risk for the sake of an overtrick. This will apply mainly on deals where no sharp bidding decisions have to be taken, where the final contract is obvious and easy to reach.

Fundamentals

♠ J 7 6 4 3
♡ K 6 5
♢ A Q 10 4
♣ J

East-West game
Dealer South

South	North
1 ♠	4 ♠

♠ A K 10 8 5 2
♡ A 7 2
♢ 7 6
♣ 8 5

West leads the king of clubs against what will surely be the standard contract, and East plays the seven. West switches to the knave of hearts, and you win with dummy's king while East follows with the nine. One round suffices to draw the trumps, and a finesse of the ten of diamonds loses to the knave. The three of hearts comes back, and West plays the four under your ace. What now?

A successful finesse of the queen of diamonds will give you an overtrick, but if the finesse fails East will cash a heart and you will be one down. This is clearly a top or bottom affair and the odds of 52 per cent on the finesse are not particularly attractive. Since everyone is likely to be in this contract, however, the finesse would perhaps be worth risking if there were no other way of trying to make an overtrick.

But here there is quite a sound alternative play. Instead of taking a second diamond finesse you should play a diamond to the ace and ruff dummy's small diamond, hoping for the king to drop in three rounds. This play gives a reduced chance of making the overtrick, but at least it ensures ten tricks. On balance you are less likely to get a bad score by this method.

If North's original diamond holding were A J 10 4 instead of A Q 10 4, the position would be very different.

Dummy Play

♠ J 7 6 4 3
♡ K 6 5
♢ A J 10 4   *East-West game*
♣ J   *Dealer South*

	South	North
♠ A K 10 8 5 2 | 1 ♠ | 4 ♠ |
♡ A 7 2
♢ 7 6
♣ 8 5

Assume the same opening lead and similar play up to the point where you have to decide whether or not to take a second finesse in diamonds.

In this case the second finesse will work more than 68 per cent of the time.

Since the overall chances of making more than one trick by taking two finesses are the same (76 per cent) for each combination, it seems strange that the second finesse should have so much better a chance on this hand than on the last. The basic reason is that with the queen combination you used up a larger slice of your chances on the first round. The losing finesse of the ten used up 50 of the overall 76 per cent, leaving 26 out of the remaining 50, i.e. 52 per cent, for the second finesse.

With the knave combination only 24 of the overall 76 per cent were used on the first round (the chance of West having both honours). That leaves 52 out of the remaining 76, i.e. 68·4 per cent, for the second finesse.

The same alternative play of trying to ruff out the remaining diamond honour is available, but this time it is inferior. Even 100 per cent safety cannot compensate for the greatly reduced chance of making the overtrick. You should therefore hold your breath and take a second diamond finesse. On balance this will give you more good scores and fewer bad ones than those who play safe.

Fundamentals

♠ 8 7 5
♡ 6 4 3 2
◇ A 7 5 4
♣ A J

Game all
Dealer South

	South	*North*
♠ K Q	2 NT	3 NT
♡ A K Q 9 5		
◇ K 8 2		
♣ K 8 6		

West leads the ten of spades against your three no trump contract, and East produces the knave. How should you plan the play?

This contract is not so good. No doubt partner thought he had his reasons, but his decision not to inquire about suits was more than a little eccentric. It is unlikely that anyone else will play this hand in three no trumps. The other pairs will all be in four hearts, and you can see that they will all chalk up 650 for eleven tricks, losing just one spade and one diamond. In no trumps, unhappily, only ten top tricks are available.

This is one of the occasions where you have to keep faith with your miserable bidding and assume that the par is five no trumps, not five hearts. And the only way to make eleven tricks at no trumps is to play West for the queen of clubs and take the finesse.

It is important to realize that the hazardous-looking finesse of the knave of clubs in reality risks nothing at all. If the finesse fails you may go down in your contract, certainly. But the zero you get for going down in your contract will not be any larger or rounder than the zero you expect for making four no trumps while everyone else is making five hearts.

The finesse gives you a fifty-fifty chance of converting a bottom into a top.

Dummy Play

♠ Q 7 6 3
♡ 6 2
◇ Q J 8 5
♣ J 10 4

	Love all	
	Dealer South	
	South	North
♠ A K J	2 NT	3 ♣
♡ Q J 8	3 NT	—
◇ K 7 3		
♣ A K 9 3		

West leads the five of hearts against your three no trump contract. East wins with the ace and returns the nine of hearts, and your knave holds the trick when West follows with the three. How do you plan the play?

Partner has at least learned to ask about suits, although it didn't help on this hand. In spite of your combined total of twenty-seven points, the prospect of nine tricks seems remote. The hearts appear to be 5–3 and the defenders have maintained communication in the suit, so it is immaterial which of them has the ace of diamonds. If you lead a diamond you will be one down.

Since West is known to have the long hearts, the odds are five to four on East having the queen of clubs. But in order to finesse in clubs you would have to overtake the knave of spades, so the spades would have to break 3–3 as well for you to make your contract. The probability of both these factors being right is no more than 20 per cent, and you have to balance that against the 45 per cent chance of West having the queen of clubs in which case you would be at least two down.

The odds against success are too great. Your primary concern, remember, is not to make your contract, but to outscore the other pairs. Everyone will be in this three no trump contract, and since the defence seems fairly automatic they will all have the same problem. On balance it is best to lead a diamond and go peacefully one down. You are more likely to score above average this way than by trying to make the contract.

Fundamentals

♠ J 7 4
♡ A 10 7 3
♢ Q J 9 6
♣ 9 2

Game all
Dealer South

♠ A K
♡ 9 5 4
♢ 10 3
♣ A K Q 10 8 3

South	North
1 ♣	1 ♢
3 ♣	—

West leads the two of hearts against your three club contract. How should you play?

Your bidding appears to have slipped below par on this hand. It is unfortunate that both you and your partner chose to be conservative at the same time. Either of you might have had a shot at three no trumps on the second round.

You are likely to be alone or nearly alone in your misfortune, for most pairs will manage to drag themselves up to three no trumps one way or another, and it is clear that they will make nine tricks if clubs behave normally.

The only chance of salvaging some match-points on the board is to assume that the clubs will break badly. If West has four or five clubs to the knave the three no trumpers will go one down. So will you in your three club contract, but at least that will make it an average board.

What if East has four or five clubs to the knave? Then three no trumps could be made by double-dummy play, but in practice the declarers will go one down. But by playing for this bad break you will be able to make your three club contract and score a top.

The best play, therefore, is to win the first trick and run the nine of clubs from dummy. This will give you a zero instead of perhaps one match-point 36 per cent of the time (when West has J, J x, or J x x), but it will convert an average into a top 14 per cent of the time (when West has a small singleton or void).

Dummy Play

♠ 10 9 6 4
♡ A 9 7 6
◇ K Q
♣ 8 5 2

Love all
Dealer North

	North	South
♠ A K J 5	—	1 ♠
♡ 5 4 3	3 ♠	—
◇ A 9 4		
♣ 10 7 6		

West leads the king of clubs against your three spade contract and East encourages with the nine. East wins the second round with the ace and returns a club to his partner's queen. West then switches to the knave of hearts. How should you play?

You'll really have to think about getting a new partner. This one should surely have allowed for the possibility of a light third-hand opening. Two spades is the bid which any reasonable North player will make, and two spades is the contract most pairs will play in.

There appears to be very little chance of making nine tricks. The only hope would be to find a blockage in the heart position, but on West's lead of the knave this seems remote.

One down in three spades will be a hideous result if two spades makes at the other tables. The only chance of picking up a few points lies in assuming that two spades will normally be defeated. The declarers in two spades will make the routine percentage play of taking the spade finesse on the second round, and if West has the queen they will go down.

To tie their score of minus fifty you must assume the spade queen to be doubleton and go against the odds by refusing the spade finesse. Instead play out the ace and king. If it is your lucky day the queen will drop from West and you will get an average score.

3

Defence

IN many ways pairs is the toughest form of bridge, and defence is certainly the toughest part of the pairs game. A defensive pairs session, when opponents hold most of the cards and you hardly get to play the dummy at all, can be a traumatic experience.

The pressure on the defenders at pairs is unrelenting. Even when you have defeated the enemy contract you cannot afford to take things easy, for a one trick set may not be enough to earn a good score. It may be necessary to beat the contract by two tricks, or even three. When it is clear that the declarer can make his contract with something to spare, you still cannot afford to relax your concentration for an instant. Every trick counts. Holding declarer to ten tricks rather than allowing him to make eleven is sure to make a big difference to your match-point score.

We have seen that the declarer must evaluate his contract in order that he may make the correct match-point decisions in the play of the hand. It is vastly more difficult for the defenders to do this, since they do not know the exact strength and distribution of the declarer's hand and can only hazard a guess at the correct match-point contract. Nevertheless, as the play progresses the defenders must try to evaluate the contract, for it is only thus that they can decide how many tricks they will need to score well.

Defence

Setting a target of tricks like this will not usually be possible before the opening lead. The sight of dummy will help, though, and it will sometimes be possible for one or other of the defenders to set a provisional target after the first trick. On other occasions you will not be able to make a decision until a later stage in the play.

Often you will be confronted by a cash-out situation, where it is clear that you must take your tricks quickly before the declarer can get discards. In such cases close partnership co-operation will be required to be sure of making all the tricks that are available to the defence.

The decision whether to try to defeat the contract or just to concentrate on preventing overtricks will often be a close one. At team or rubber bridge your sole aim is to defeat the contract, and you are justified in taking such risks as may be necessary to accomplish this aim. At pairs your prime concern is not to defeat the contract but to achieve a better score than the other pairs holding your cards. The chance of defeating the contract must be balanced against the risk of allowing the declarer to make an overtrick. In general it is conservative defence that is more likely to produce the better score in such situations.

All defence is based upon certain assumptions which you make about the declarer's holding. At pairs you must make sure that your assumptions conform to the peculiar logic of match-point scoring. At the critical point in any hand there will usually be alternative lines of defence for you to choose between. One line may be based on the assumption that declarer has a particular card, but if the presence of that card in declarer's hand means that a superior match-point contract would be available you can afford to forget about that line of defence. Always consider the consequences of any assumption you are about to make from the match-point angle. Then perhaps you will change your mind.

One of the main requirements for effective defence is clear and unambiguous signalling. This was forgotten in the hand overleaf with fatal result.

Fundamentals

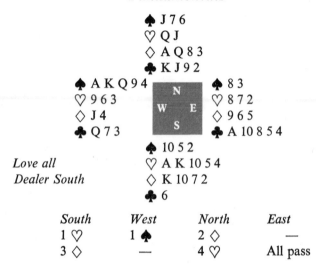

```
                    ♠ J 7 6
                    ♡ Q J
                    ◇ A Q 8 3
                    ♣ K J 9 2
        ♠ A K Q 9 4   N        ♠ 8 3
        ♡ 9 6 3                ♡ 8 7 2
        ◇ J 4     W   E        ◇ 9 6 5
        ♣ Q 7 3       S        ♣ A 10 8 5 4
                    ♠ 10 5 2
Love all            ♡ A K 10 5 4
Dealer South        ◇ K 10 7 2
                    ♣ 6
```

South	West	North	East
1 ♡	1 ♠	2 ◇	—
3 ◇	—	4 ♡	All pass

The defence started off with three rounds of spades, and East produced a mini-signal by discarding the five of clubs.

West studied this card and concluded that it was his partner's lowest club. The declarer appeared to be marked with the ace of clubs anyway, for on the bidding he must surely have all fourteen of the missing points. It seemed to West, therefore, that the only chance of another trick was to play his partner for four trumps to the ten. Yes, you've guessed it. West continued with a fourth round of spades, and the declarer gratefully ruffed in dummy and discarded his losing club.

East explained that he was not sure if South had a third spade, and he did not wish to simplify any guess the declarer might have to make in the club suit. There are, of course, times when a clumsy signal can only help declarer, but the argument hardly holds water in this case. With a doubleton spade, declarer would know West had six to the three top honours and would be unlikely to misguess the clubs.

In view of the strong dummy East should have realized that his partner would not expect him to have an ace, and he should have signalled its presence as vigorously as possible.

Defence

♠ K 5
♡ Q 5 3 2
◇ A K Q 10 4
♣ Q 4

Game all
Dealer North

♠ A J 6
♡ J 10 9 7
◇ 7 6 3
♣ K J 10

North	South
1 ◇	1 NT
2 NT	3 NT

Your partner leads the four of spades and you capture dummy's king with your ace. The knave holds the second trick, and on the third round partner's queen takes declarer's ten while a heart is thrown from dummy. West continues with the nine of spades, on which dummy throws a second heart, you the three of diamonds and South the three of clubs. On the last spade a third heart is thrown from dummy. What do you discard?

The contract is already one down, but of course you want to do better. There are three outstanding high cards—the ace of clubs and the two top hearts—and partner is sure to have one of them. To discard the knave of clubs might cost a trick if partner has the ace of clubs, but it does not pay to be too greedy. Whatever your partner's honour card, you want a club switch, and you should make this clear by discarding the knave.

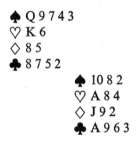

♠ Q 9 7 4 3
♡ K 6
◇ 8 5
♣ 8 7 5 2

♠ 10 8 2
♡ A 8 4
◇ J 9 2
♣ A 9 6 3

Note that if you discard the ambiguous seven of hearts West might decide to play you for the ace of clubs. If he leads the king of hearts to pin dummy's queen, declarer will have a club-heart squeeze against you and will escape for one down.

57

Fundamentals

Game all
Dealer South

♠ Q 10 7 2
♡ J 10 9 5
♢ Q 5 2
♣ K 7

South	North
1 ♢	1 ♡
1 ♠	2 ♠
—	

♠ 5 4
♡ A K 6
♢ A 9 7 6
♣ 10 8 5 2

West leads the three of diamonds against South's two spade contract. How do you plan the defence?

Partner's card is an obvious singleton and you will clearly try to give him two diamond ruffs. Are you thinking of cashing the king of hearts at trick two to show partner where your entry lies? After doing that you might find that you no longer have an entry. Naturally you hope to be able to make two heart tricks, but you should be prepared to find that you have only one.

The sure way of taking the maximum number of defensive tricks is by using the Lavinthal suit preference signal. At trick two you should return the nine of diamonds, your highest remaining card in the suit, to request a switch to the higher-ranking side suit. Partner will ruff and lead a heart to your king. After a second diamond ruff he will cash the ace of clubs if he has it before leading another heart.

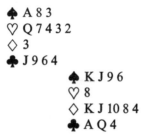

♠ A 8 3
♡ Q 7 4 3 2
♢ 3
♣ J 9 6 4

♠ K J 9 6
♡ 8
♢ K J 10 8 4
♣ A Q 4

Correct defence just holds South to his contract in this case. Anyone who cashed the king of hearts at trick two would end up with a score of minus 140, which is sure to be bad.

Defence

♠ J 10 7 2
♡ A 5 3
♦ A 10
♣ K J 9 5

East-West game
Dealer South

South	North		
1 ♡	1 ♠		♠ A 8 6 5
2 ♦	3 NT		♡ 10 4
4 ♦	4 ♡		♦ 8
			♣ Q 10 8 7 4 3

Against South's four heart contract West leads the king of spades which holds the trick. He continues with a small spade to your ace, but South ruffs. A trump is led to the ace and two more rounds drawn with the king and queen, your partner following with small cards each time. What is your trick target and how should you defend?

You know that declarer has at least ten cards in the red suits, and the fact that he has drawn trumps immediately can only mean that his diamonds are solid. If declarer has the ace of clubs he will make twelve tricks, but if not you should be able to hold him to eleven. Two tricks is the maximum for the defence, for even if South has two small clubs your partner's ace will be single and South will be saved a guess in the suit.

On this bidding, however, it is not impossible for South to have six diamonds. Then he will have a singleton club, and partner will have a tough decision to make when it is led. Perhaps at this very moment partner is steeling himself to play low smoothly if a club is led. That will never do. You must throw him an immediate lifeline by discarding your queen of clubs on the third trump.

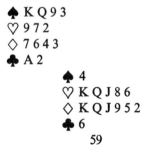

♠ K Q 9 3
♡ 9 7 2
♦ 7 6 4 3
♣ A 2

♠ 4
♡ K Q J 8 6
♦ K Q J 9 5 2
♣ 6

Fundamentals

		♠ 9 4
Love all		♡ K J 10 3
Dealer South		◇ K Q J 2
		♣ J 10 7

South	*North*	♠ K 3
1 ♠	2 ◇	♡ 8 7 5
2 ♡	3 ♡	◇ A 8 6 4
3 ♠	4 ♡	♣ A K 8 3

Your partner leads the two of clubs against South's four heart contract and you win with the king. How should you continue?

On the bidding the declarer is marked with a 6–4 holding in the major suits. He will therefore have three cards in the minors, and your immediate target must be to cash your three winners as safely as possible. There is no need to worry about the spade position. If you have a trick in the suit it cannot run away.

If South has two clubs and a singleton diamond it could be fatal for you to continue with ace and another club. After drawing trumps South might then be able to discard all four of dummy diamonds on his spades. On the other hand it could be disastrous to try to cash the ace of diamonds if declarer is void.

In such cases you cannot be sure of the correct order in which to cash your tricks, and you must therefore pass the decision to your partner. Given a count of the club suit by your return of the three of clubs at the second trick, partner will be in no doubt. If he started with four clubs he will lead a diamond. With only three clubs he will return a club to your ace.

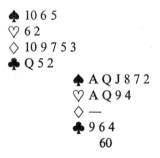

```
        ♠ 10 6 5
        ♡ 6 2
        ◇ 10 9 7 5 3
        ♣ Q 5 2
                    ♠ A Q J 8 7 2
                    ♡ A Q 9 4
                    ◇ —
                    ♣ 9 6 4
```

Defence

♠ Q J 7 3
♡ K Q J 8
◇ A J 5
♣ A 8

North-South game
Dealer North

North	South
1 ♡	1 ♠
4 ♠	—

♠ K 4
♡ 7 6 5 3
◇ K Q 4
♣ Q 10 6 4

Your lead of the four of clubs is won by dummy's ace, partner playing the two. The queen of spades is then led and allowed to run to your king. What is your trick target and what should you lead now?

Since declarer appears to have the king of clubs it is likely that your partner has one of the major suit aces; with both South would surely have gone on over North's four spade bid. That gives the defence two tricks, and to defeat the contract you would require two tricks in diamonds. If South has three diamonds to the nine, he would probably guess wrong if you led the four of diamonds and partner's ten would score.

That is certainly the way you would defend in a rubber or team game, because there is nothing else to try. At pairs, however, the play is much too risky. Declarer is unlikely to have exactly three diamonds to the nine. He could equally well have three small diamonds, three to the ten, or a doubleton, and with any of these holdings he would make an overtrick if you lead a small diamond.

On this hand the sensible course is to limit your target to three tricks and lead the king of diamonds.

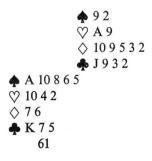

♠ 9 2
♡ A 9
◇ 10 9 5 3 2
♣ J 9 3 2

♠ A 10 8 6 5
♡ 10 4 2
◇ 7 6
♣ K 7 5

Fundamentals

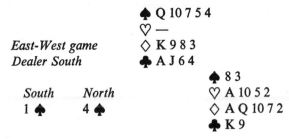

```
                    ♠ Q 10 7 5 4
                    ♡ —
East-West game      ◇ K 9 8 3
Dealer South        ♣ A J 6 4
                              ♠ 8 3
  South    North              ♡ A 10 5 2
   1 ♠      4 ♠               ◇ A Q 10 7 2
                              ♣ K 9
```

West leads the four of hearts against South's four spade contract. The declarer ruffs in dummy and draws trumps with the ace and king, West throwing the three of hearts on the second round. Next comes the queen of clubs which runs to your king. How should you continue?

At this point you have to decide whether to cash your ace of diamonds or not. If you do not take it now, declarer may be able to get rid of his diamonds on dummy's clubs. On the other hand you will not wish to limit yourself to two defensive tricks if there is any chance of making a third.

On such occasions a count of the declarer's tricks will usually tell you what to do. In this case South has five trump tricks plus three ruffs in dummy. Even if he has three club tricks that adds up to only eleven, so there is no need to press the panic button. Declarer will always have to concede a diamond or a heart at the end, and you may be able to hold him to his contract.

You must not return a heart, for this might allow South either to score the king immediately or to produce an end-play for an extra trick. The passive nine of clubs is the proper return.

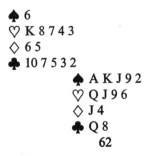

```
    ♠ 6
    ♡ K 8 7 4 3
    ◇ 6 5
    ♣ 10 7 5 3 2
              ♠ A K J 9 2
              ♡ Q J 9 6
              ◇ J 4
              ♣ Q 8
```

Defence

♠ A K 4
♡ A 7
◇ 9 8 4 2
♣ Q 9 7 4

	Game all		Dealer East
	West North		East South
♠ 7 5			— —
♡ K 6 5 3 2	—	1 NT	— 2 ♣
◇ A 10 5	—	2 ◇	— 2 ♠
♣ J 10 6	All pass		

On your opening lead of the knave of clubs dummy plays the four, partner the five, and declarer the three. You continue with the ten of clubs, covered by the queen and king and ruffed by South. The ace and king of spades are cashed and East echoes with the ten and nine. The ace and another heart come next, East following with the four and the knave. South covers with the queen and your king wins. How do you continue?

It looks as though partner has the master queen of trumps. The trouble is he will never get in to cash it. He can hardly have the king or queen of diamonds or he would have opened the bidding but it is just possible that he has the knave. You know that declarer started with five spades, four hearts and a singleton club, and therefore three diamonds. The count tells you that it is perfectly safe to underlead your diamond ace in an attempt to hold the declarer to eight tricks. If partner has the knave, the declarer will have time to discard only one of dummy's diamonds on his good hearts, for partner will ruff with his master trump and lead another diamond through.

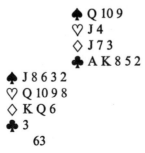

♠ Q 10 9
♡ J 4
◇ J 7 3
♣ A K 8 5 2

♠ J 8 6 3 2
♡ Q 10 9 8
◇ K Q 6
♣ 3

Fundamentals

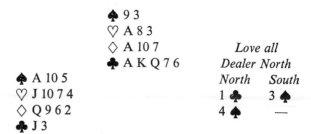

♠ 9 3
♡ A 8 3
◇ A 10 7
♣ A K Q 7 6

♠ A 10 5
♡ J 10 7 4
◇ Q 9 6 2
♣ J 3

Love all
Dealer North

North	South
1 ♣	3 ♠
4 ♠	—

You lead the knave of hearts against South's four spade contract, and partner plays the nine under dummy's ace. South leads a spade to his king and you allow him to hold the trick. You win the queen of spades with your ace, and East discards the knave of diamonds. What is your trick target and how should you continue?

Even without seeing partner's knave of diamonds you would expect him to have the king, for South has shown enough for his bidding. Declarer has six trump tricks which, with the five tricks visible on the table, add up to eleven, so at first glance it appears that you should limit your defensive target to two tricks —a trump and a heart. This is not necessarily so, however.

One thing you can be sure about is that South does not have a singleton club, for in that case he would have gone after immediate discards. South is also unlikely to have a red singleton, for with a five-card suit your partner might well have ventured an overcall at the one-level. Declarer's probable distribution is 7–2–2–2, and in that case the defence can make three tricks. You must lead a diamond immediately to give South communication trouble. He will have to win and play out three rounds of clubs, and you will make your trump as well as a red suit trick.

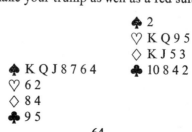

♠ 2
♡ K Q 9 5
◇ K J 5 3
♣ 10 8 4 2

♠ K Q J 8 7 6 4
♡ 6 2
◇ 8 4
♣ 9 5

Defence

		♠ A K J
		♡ 10 8 3
Game all		◇ A K 4
Dealer North		♣ K 10 6 4
North	*South*	♠ 8 7 5
1 ♣	1 ◇	♡ Q J 9 7
2 NT	3 ◇	◇ Q 2
—		♣ A Q 9 5

West leads the eight of clubs against South's three diamond contract, dummy plays low and your queen wins. This particular partner would have led the middle card from three small clubs, so you know that you can give him a ruff. How should you play?

You have a choice between making sure of three tricks by playing the ace and another club immediately, or trying to defeat the contract by leading the queen of hearts at trick two. The latter play risks allowing the declarer to make eleven tricks.

In such cases you should try to evaluate declarer's contract from the match-point angle. On the bidding South is likely to have six diamonds, and if he has the ace of hearts three no trumps will be on ice. Some pairs are likely to be in it, so in this case there is no need to worry too much about taking the maximum in defence against three diamonds.

But if South has the king of hearts, three no trumps is likely to go down on the natural lead of the queen of hearts. So you must make sure that three diamonds also goes down and the queen of hearts is the proper card to lead at trick two.

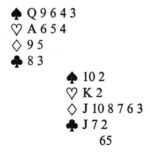

```
          ♠ Q 9 6 4 3
          ♡ A 6 5 4
          ◇ 9 5
          ♣ 8 3
                    ♠ 10 2
                    ♡ K 2
                    ◇ J 10 8 7 6 3
                    ♣ J 7 2
```

Fundamentals

♠ K Q J 7 5 4
♡ 9 7 2
♢ 8
♣ K Q J

Game all
Dealer South

♠ 8 3
♡ K 10 8 4 3
♢ 10 6
♣ A 10 7 4

South	North
1 NT	3 NT
(12–14)	

On your lead of the four of hearts partner plays the queen and South the ace. Declarer leads the five of clubs and you take the ace, East following with the two. How do you continue?

Clearly North was in a gambling mood and hoped the hand would produce as many tricks in no trumps as in spades. You will get a poor score if the gamble comes off, for most pairs will be in the spade game. Declarer has at least nine tricks established now, for he will certainly have the ace of spades to play like this.

There are two reasonable lines of defence. One is to lead a diamond in the hope that partner has the ace and can lead another heart through. The alternative is to hope that the knave of hearts is now bare. There are no clues in the bidding or play to date, but there is a good match-point reason for leading a diamond.

If declarer has the ace of diamonds and started with A J bare in hearts, the hand will probably play for eleven tricks in spades, and it will therefore be no tragedy to allow the declarer to make an unmakable ten tricks in no trumps. When declarer has three hearts and lacks the ace of diamonds, on the other hand, four spades may be beaten on a heart lead, and you must make sure that three no trumps is beaten too.

♠ 10 2
♡ Q 5
♢ A J 9 5 4 2
♣ 8 3 2

♠ A 9 6
♡ A J 6
♢ K Q 7 3
♣ 9 6 5

66

PART TWO

Contesting the Part-Score

4

Bidding

Survival of the Fittest

ROUGHLY one-third of all the deals that come your way will be competitive part-score deals, and this group is of particular importance in the pairs game. When the high-card strength of the pack is fairly evenly divided, both sides can often make a part-score contract and the bidding becomes a tooth-and-claw struggle to get the better of the enemy. Good players feel at home in this part-score jungle where superior judgement offers many opportunities for beating par.

The first essential is to modify your bidding methods to enable you to get into the auction whenever there is a reasonable prospect of there being a contract of some sort for your side. Overcalls are made with less regard for the safety factor than in other forms of bridge, because the risks are different. At total points you may risk a penalty of 500 only if there is a good chance of game for one side or the other, but at pairs it is as important not to let the enemy do you out of a part-score as it is to stop them stealing your game.

All overcalls are inherently risky, because the opponents have beaten you to the punch and achieved a superior competitive position, but there are grave risks in passing too. The risk of getting the chopper from your left-hand opponent must be weighed against the risk of losing the part-score battle. The amount of the penalty you risk hardly enters into the matter. It is your estimate of the probability of gain versus loss that will determine your action.

Contesting the Part-Score

Vulnerability is a vital factor in all competitive bidding. At favourable vulnerability, that is when the opponents are vulnerable and you are not, it is a moral certainty that you will not be doubled at the one-level, and you can therefore take a good deal of licence with your overcalls in this situation. Possession of the spade suit is, as always, the greatest possible asset.

(a) ♠ J 10 9 5 3	(b) ♠ K 10 9 3
♡ 7 2	♡ 9 8 4
◇ A 10 8 5	◇ A 9 7 4 2
♣ 6 5	♣ 4

If your right-hand opponent opens one club, both the above hands are worth an overcall of one spade. The most effective overcalls are those that take away the maximum bidding space from the opponents. Here the one spade overcall prevents a natural response of one heart from the opener's partner. If he has a heart suit he may stretch to show it at the two-level. His response will still be forcing on the opener, and they may well get too high.

If the opening bid is one heart, an overcall of one spade removes no bidding space from the opponents and so has less to gain. It might still be worth risking on hand (a), but on (b) it would be wiser to pass. Length in the enemy suit, even three cards, should always be regarded as a danger sign. It increases the chance that opener's partner will be short in the suit, and therefore long in your suit. The hand could be a misfit all round, and on misfit hands the best course is to stay out of the auction and allow the opponents to get into trouble. The evidence of a misfit is, of course, very slender at this stage and will be completely reversed if the opener's partner supports hearts. But if responder's raise to two hearts is passed round you can think again and compete with a bid of two spades.

At the two-level the chance of being doubled is clearly greater, and a little more playing strength is needed to make an overcall. Nevertheless, overcalls are often made on hands that would be passed at other forms of bridge.

Bidding

(a) ♠ 7
   ♡ K J 8 6 5 2
   ◇ A 6 4
   ♣ J 9 3

(b) ♠ J 9 3
   ♡ K J 8 6 5 2
   ◇ A 6 4
   ♣ 7

If your right-hand opponent opens one spade, hand (a) is a minimum non-vulnerable overcall of two hearts. This may produce a bad result when the trumps are stacked behind you, but the risk is worth taking. More often you will find a fit with partner and be able to contest the part-score.

Hand (b) is the same with the black suit holdings transposed. Once again the possession of three cards in the enemy suit acts as a deterrent and tips the balance against the overcall. The chance of conceding a penalty this time outweighs the prospect of finding a fit, and the wise course is to pass and await developments.

When you are vulnerable the opponents will be tempted to double you much more readily, since to defeat you by just one trick will give them a better score than making a part-score contract of their own. At unfavourable vulnerability overcalls are especially risky, for a penalty of 500 for two down doubled will more than compensate your opponents for abandoning their non-vulnerable game. Vulnerable overcalls at the two-level should therefore be at least as good in playing strength at pairs as at rubber bridge.

(c) ♠ 4
   ♡ A Q J 9 7 3
   ◇ K Q 10 3
   ♣ 6 5

(d) ♠ 9 2
   ♡ 7
   ◇ K J 10 9 5 3
   ♣ A K 8 7

The above hands are about the minimum for two-level overcalls at unfavourable vulnerability.

By far the safest way to get into the bidding is by making a takeout double. It is also the best way when the conditions are right, for by giving your partner a choice of suit you increase your chances of landing in the right spot.

Contesting the Part-Score

(a) ♠ —
  ♡ K J 7 4
  ◇ K 9 6 5 2
  ♣ K 10 8 3

(b) ♠ K 10 5 4
  ♡ 3
  ◇ A J 7 2
  ♣ K 7 6 2

At pairs the requirements for the takeout double are shaded on distributional hands, and most aggressive players would double one spade on (a) and one heart on (b) at any vulnerability. Of course, if you are going to double on this sort of hand your partner must not leave the double in for penalties without five or six tricks, mostly in trumps.

Note that the above hands have ideal distribution with good support for any suit partner may bid. The further away you get from the ideal distribution the more high card strength you require to double. If support for one suit is mediocre or completely lacking, considerable high-card compensation is required.

(c) ♠ 7 3
  ♡ K 9 4
  ◇ A J 8 7
  ♣ A 8 6 3

(d) ♠ 2
  ♡ A Q J 7 6
  ◇ K 8
  ♣ K Q 6 4 3

(e) ♠ 5
  ♡ A 9
  ◇ K Q J 6
  ♣ A Q 10 5 4 2

If your right-hand opponent opens one spade, each of the above hands is worth a double. On (c) you are rock bottom minimum for the distribution, and you will pass any non-forcing bid from your partner. You can just about tolerate a heart response although, remembering that partner will strain to bid any four-card major suit, you will not be too happy about it.

On (d) you are strong enough to bid two hearts over partner's expected response of two diamonds.

When you will need to rebid at the three-level over partner's likely response, even greater strength is required as in hand (e).

Some players like to double on balanced hands with 13 or 14 points, but I do not recommend this practice.

♠ K 9 5
♡ A J 7
◇ Q 6 5 3
♣ K J 2

Bidding

If you double an opposing one bid with this hand you may occasionally land on your feet but you are much more likely to get into trouble. You have no ruffing values to assist your partner in a suit contract, and such strength as you have is mainly defensive in nature. It is much better to pass on such hands.

An even worse practice is that of doubling on distributional hands that have both length and strength in the enemy suit.

♠ A Q 9 4
♡ K 3
♢ A Q 9 7 6
♣ 6 3

To double one spade on the above hand is to get the worst of both worlds. Not only do you bail the enemy out of trouble but you will usually land up on your left ear. Nor is an overcall of two diamonds the right answer. Why stick your neck out on what has every appearance of being a misfit hand? If you force me at gunpoint to take some action on this hand the bid I would choose is one no trumps. But I would much rather pass, especially if the opponents are vulnerable.

What is commonly called the trap pass is the only sensible action on all hands with length in the enemy suit up to about the 18-point mark. I don't much care for the term 'trap pass', since it does not accurately reflect the philosophy behind the action. The connotations of malice and low cunning give a completely false impression. You do not deliberately refrain from making the normal bid in an attempt to lure old George to his doom. Certainly you will be well placed to wield the chopper if George gets too high, but your pass is made simply because there is no positive action that properly expresses your values. On such hands it is always dangerous to bid. The pass offers the best chance of a good score.

(a) ♠ K J 6 3
♡ A Q 9 2
♢ 4
♣ K Q 5 4

(b) ♠ A Q J 3 2
♡ K J
♢ K 10 8 7 3
♣ 9

(c) ♠ J 10 8 6 3 2
♡ 5 4
♢ A K
♣ A K Q

Contesting the Part-Score

Each of these hands rates a smooth pass over an enemy bid of one spade. On none of them is there a sensible alternative. On (*a*) you would pass an opening bid of one club or one heart with equal alacrity, but you would double one diamond. On (*b*) you would pass an opening bid of one diamond but double one club. Over one heart the choice between a double and a simple overcall of one spade would be close—a matter of style more than anything. On (*c*) you would double any opening bid other than one spade.

The key to the proper action over an enemy opening bid can be expressed quite simply in one sentence. Be bold and aggressive when short in the enemy suit, but keep quiet when long. If there is any one secret of successful competitive bidding, this is it. Adherence to this principle will bring you out on the right side of par time and time again.

Reopening the Bidding

Since your partner is going to pass quite strong hands with length in the enemy suit, it follows that when your left-hand opponent's opening bid is followed by two passes you must keep the bidding alive on fairly light values. It is normal to make light protective or balancing bids in this position at any form of bridge, but in the pairs game values tend to be stretched even further because of the pressing need to contest the part-score.

(*a*) ♠ K Q 10 7 5	(*b*) ♠ J 9 4	(*c*) ♠ 7 2
♡ 7	♡ 9 2	♡ 4
◇ 9 8 4 3	◇ 6 3	◇ K Q J 9 5 4
♣ 8 7 4	♣ A J 10 7 6 3	♣ A Q 6 3

(*d*) ♠ K 9 3	(*e*) ♠ 10 8 7 4	(*f*) ♠ Q J 6
♡ 7 6 5	♡ 8	♡ A J 3
◇ Q 10 7 2	◇ A Q 3	◇ K 10 6 2
♣ A K 8	♣ K 9 6 5 4	♣ K Q 4

If an opening bid of one heart by your left-hand opponent is

Bidding

passed round to you, action should be taken with each of these hands.

With (*a*) you should bid one spade. Normally a simple overcall shows from about seven points to a bad twelve. Here you are stretching pretty far, but it does not pay to allow the opponents to play at the one-level in such cases.

On (*b*) bid two clubs. This is again a minimum hand for the bid. The good suit compensates for the shortage of points.

On (*c*) bid three diamonds. You are too good for a simple overcall and must jump to show your values.

With (*d*) one no trumps is the bid. This shows a balanced hand of 11–14 points and does not guarantee a stopper in the enemy suit. Partner will not raise without something in hearts.

On (*e*) you should double. The double is made with upwards of nine points and shortage in the enemy suit. This is the ideal way of reopening since it gives partner the opportunity to pass for penalties.

Double is again the call on (*f*). You are too strong for a reopening one no trump bid and must double first. This may create a problem if partner replies with two of a minor suit. It could be right to pass this, but most red-blooded pairs players will risk' two no trumps.

In cases where you are in doubt as to whether to protect or not, a reference to your holding in the enemy suit will usually decide the issue.

♠ 6				
♡ K Q 9 7 4	*West*	*North*	*East*	*South*
◊ J 10 4 2	1 ◊	—	—	?
♣ 8 7 5				

It looks natural enough to protect with a bid of one heart, but the length in diamonds should deter you. Partner is marked with quite a strong hand and yet he failed to overcall. He can hardly have great length in diamonds himself, and so he must clearly have a balanced hand. No doubt you can make some heart contract, but there is little chance of your being allowed to play in it.

Contesting the Part-Score

The opponents certainly have a spade fit and they will find it if you bid. The proper course is to pass and let West struggle in one diamond.

♠ 9 8 6 4				
♡ 10 3	*West*	*North*	*East*	*South*
◇ 5 4	1 ♠	—	—	?
♣ A K J 9 3				

Once again the sensible action is to pass. Partner is likely to have a balanced 10–14 points, and the opponents might well find a better contract in one of the red suits if you gave them a chance.

Misfit Hands

The question of bidding misfit hands can be summed up succinctly in one word—don't. Such hands invariably result in a poor score for the declarer's side, and it is the pair who are quickest in getting out of the bidding who come out on top.

♠ 9		*Game all. Dealer West*		
♡ K Q 9 5 3	*West*	*North*	*East*	*South*
◇ J 7 6 2	1 ◇	1 ♠	2 ♣	?
♣ K 10 4				

You should not consider a bid of two hearts on the above holding. All the indications are that the hand is a misfit, and a pass is the only sound action.

♠ A K J 8 4	*South*	*West*	*North*	*East*
♡ A J 3	1 ♠	2 ♣	—	2 ♡
◇ 5	?			
♣ Q 10 6 3				

At any vulnerability you should be happy to pass on the second round. It looks like a misfit hand, and to rebid two spades could be fatal. Partner can always show delayed support for spades if he has it, and if he has not it is better to let the opponents struggle with the misfit.

Bidding

Sometimes, of course, the opponents will be quicker off their marks and you will be left holding the baby. When that happens the only thing to do is to stop bidding as soon as the misfit is diagnosed. Trying to improve the contract usually leads to disaster.

♠ J 10 8 4				
♡ 6	*North*	*East*	*South*	*West*
◇ K 7 3	1 ♡	—	2 ♣	2 ◇
♣ A Q 9 5 4	2 ♡	—	?	

Partner had no obligation to rebid. The fact that he did so means that he will have a good heart suit, and a pass is your only sensible course of action.

In the days before negative doubles there was a hand in a World Pairs Olympiad final where South had a difficult decision to make on the second round.

♠ A K 7 6 5 2		*Love all. Dealer North*		
♡ —	*West*	*North*	*East*	*South*
◇ 5	—	1 ♡	1 ♠	Double
♣ Q J 10 7 6 3	—	2 ♡	—	?

Even at World Championship level very few of the South players had the self-discipline to pass. Those who did were rewarded with a shared top.

When the hands are not obvious misfits there are still many occasions when a pass stands out. The commonest of these is when the opponents are clearly in a poor contract.

♠ J 4		*East-West game. Dealer South*		
♡ 10 2	*South*	*West*	*North*	*East*
◇ A 8 5	1 ♣	1 ◇	1 ♡	1 NT
♣ K Q J 10 7 4	?			

In an individual tournament the bidding started the same way at each of the five tables. Four of the South players pressed on with a bid of two clubs. They were allowed to play there and went one down for a score of minus 50. Only at one table did South make the obvious pass. West and North also passed, and the

Contesting the Part-Score

defence made five club tricks and two aces for a score of plus 100. Note that this would have been a top even if two clubs had scraped home. And had it been possible to make three clubs, one no trumps would most likely have gone two down.

Putting on the Pressure

When you have a good fit with partner you should take an active part in the bidding and hang on for as long as you can. Even when the opponents have the balance of power it does not pay to allow them to win the declaration too easily. An aggressive push or two may force them up to a level that is uncomfortably high.

The big problem is to know just how far to go, and there are two main factors which should influence your decision—(*a*) the vulnerability, and (*b*) who has the boss suit. Clearly you cannot afford to overbid more than marginally when you are vulnerable. The opponents will be quick to double, and if they defeat you by just one trick that will be worse than allowing them to make any part-score contract. Holding the higher-ranking suit gives you a great advantage, of course, for you can force the enemy up to the three-level without going beyond the two-level yourself.

It is when both vulnerability and suit-rank are in your favour that you can afford to be most aggressive in contesting the part-score.

East-West game. Dealer West

♠ K 9 6 5	*West*	*North*	*East*	*South*
♡ J 9 7 4 3	1 ◇	—	—	Double
◇ 8	2 ◇	2 ♠	—	—
♣ A J 4	3 ◇	—	—	?

Clearly West has quite a strong hand and you would normally be content to have pushed him up to the three-level. On this particular hand, however, you have good distribution combined with very little defensive strength, and this makes it worth one more effort. It is very hard to imagine three diamonds being defeated, but you would surely be unlucky not to have a play for eight tricks in spades. You should therefore bid three spades, for

78

Bidding

one down doubled will cost you only 100, less than the 110 you expect to concede if you defend against three diamonds.

The full hand:

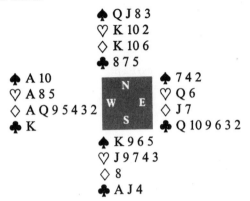

                    ♠ Q J 8 3
                    ♡ K 10 2
                    ◇ K 10 6
                    ♣ 8 7 5

♠ A 10   ♠ 7 4 2
♡ A 8 5   N   ♡ Q 6
◇ A Q 9 5 4 3 2   W   E   ◇ J 7
♣ K   S   ♣ Q 10 9 6 3 2

                    ♠ K 9 6 5
                    ♡ J 9 7 4 3
                    ◇ 8
                    ♣ A J 4

Note that the best West can do is to double your bid of three spades and accept 100 points. Three spades doubled, one down, is in fact the par result on the hand. By bidding three spades you make sure of your par, and you also put the enemy under severe pressure. There are still two ways in which you might beat par. The opponents might fail to double, which would give you a good score of minus 50, or, better still, they might press on to four diamonds. This contract would be defeated, normal defence taking a trick in each suit, and you should then have the magnificent score of plus 100.

Note also that North should not double if West bids four diamonds. He can judge from the bidding that the opponents have the balance of strength, and on such hands there is no need to double. Any plus score will be good. A double would gain little or nothing if four diamonds goes down, but would convert an average score into a bottom should four diamonds happen to make. When your side, by sacrificing against an enemy part-score, has pushed the opponents up to a higher level, you should always allow them to play undoubled.

It is often advisable to contest on quite weak hands.

79

Contesting the Part-Score

Love all. Dealer East

	West	North	East	South
♠ 7			1 ♠	—
♡ Q 8 7 4				
◊ A J 9 6 3	2 ♠	—	—	?
♣ J 6 3				

This is worth a double. The opponents no doubt have the balance of strength but they have both shown their limits and partner is marked with about ten high-card points. There is bound to be some sort of fit, and so you should make an effort to push the opponents up to the three-level.

Love all. Dealer West

	West	North	East	South
♠ K J 5			1 ♡	—
♡ 10 8 7 3	—	—		
◊ A 4	2 ♣	Double	—	2 ♠
♣ J 10 6 4	3 ♣	—	—	?

Now you should pass. Partner passed originally, and his second-round double promised good distribution rather than high-card strength. The opponents clearly have the balance of power, and in pushing them up to the three-level you have done all that is required of you.

One of the best times to apply pressure is before the opponents have been able to mention a suit.

Game all. Dealer South

	South	West	North	East
♠ K Q J 10 3	1 ♠	—	2 ♠	Double
♡ J 10 5	?			
◊ A J 10 4				
♣ 7				

You should, of course, put in an obstructive bid of three spades. You don't know whether you can make nine tricks or not, but you are unlikely to make less than eight. And even if the enemy can take 200 by doubling three spades it is by no means certain that they will. You may be permitted to play undoubled, or the opponents may play in an inferior contract at the four-level.

Bidding

There are many deals on which it is hard to tell which side has the balance of power. When the high-card points in the pack are evenly divided and the distribution is not too wild, it usually means that each side can make about eight tricks in its best suit. There will normally be both plus and minus scores on the travelling score-sheet, and it should be your aim to secure one of the pluses. The way to do that is to make your opponents play at the three-level if they insist on playing the hand.

	Game all. Dealer West			
♠ J 7 6 2	*West*	*North*	*East*	*South*
♡ A 9 7	—	—	1 ◇	—
◇ J 6 5 3	1 ♡	Double	Redouble	1 ♠
♣ Q 9	—	—	1 NT	—
	2 ◇	2 ♠	—	—
	3 ◇	—	—	?

Enough is enough. The opponents are at the three-level and it is time to pass. Don't double unless you are desperate for a top and prepared to risk a bottom. A plus score should be above average.

	Love all. Dealer South			
♠ K 7 3	*South*	*West*	*North*	*East*
♡ 4	1 ◇	Double	1 NT	2 ♡
◇ A Q 9 6 5	?			
♣ A 10 9 3				

It is dangerous to make another bid, but even more dangerous to pass and allow the enemy to play peacefully at the two-level. You should therefore bid three clubs. Minus 300 in three clubs or three diamonds doubled is less likely than minus 110 if you pass.

When to Double

In all the situations considered so far I have advised against doubling the enemy part-score contracts. However, as everyone knows, there are many occasions on which close part-score doubles ought to be made. The time to double is when *your* side has the superior strength and the opponents are trying to steal the hand.

When your side has the balance of power it is reasonable to assume that most of the pairs playing your way will register plus scores on the board. Any plus score will no longer be a good enough target in that case. You must aim to get of the larger plus scores. If the opponents get frisky and insist on sacrificing against your sure part-score contract, they must therefore be made to pay the full penalty. Rather than let them push you too high you should try for the maximum by doubling.

A penalty of 200 or 300 on a part-score hand will always be close to a top, so you can afford the occasional failure which is inevitable when you make very close doubles. The experienced match-point player expects to double his opponents into game perhaps one time in five. His doubles still show a big profit, for he scores four tops for every bottom.

		Game all. Dealer North		
♠ K 10 6	*West*	*North*	*East*	*South*
♡ K 7 5		1 ♡	1 ♠	1 NT
◇ J 10 3	2 ♠	3 ◇	—	3 ♡
♣ J 9 6 3	3 ♠	—	—	?

Your side should have the balance of power and you were fairly confident of making nine tricks in hearts. It is not likely that you can make ten, however. It is on such occasions that you try for a top by doubling.

You are by no means certain of defeating three spades, but the double risks very little. If three spades can be made, minus 140 is sure to be a poor match-point score and minus 530 will not be much worse. But plus 100 would certainly be near the bottom if most pairs are scoring plus 140 your way.

The full hand might be something like this:

Bidding

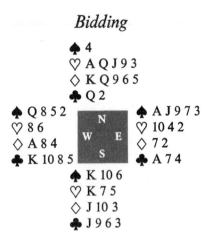

```
              ♠ 4
              ♡ A Q J 9 3
              ◇ K Q 9 6 5
              ♣ Q 2
♠ Q 8 5 2                    ♠ A J 9 7 3
♡ 8 6            N           ♡ 10 4 2
◇ A 8 4      W     E         ◇ 7 2
♣ K 10 8 5       S           ♣ A 7 4
              ♠ K 10 6
              ♡ K 7 5
              ◇ J 10 3
              ♣ J 9 6 3
```

Three hearts by North is the par contract, and West has stuck his neck out a bit too far. It is you who will fall below par if you fail to double, however.

Love all. Dealer North

	West	North	East	South
♠ 10 6		1 NT	—	2 ♡
♡ A Q 6 5 2				
◇ Q 6 4	—	—	Double	—
♣ Q 9 4	3 ◇	—	—	?

Since your partner has from 12 to 14 points your side has the balance of power, and yet it is dangerous for you to bid on. Three hearts might not make, and minus 50 would be a near-bottom. You are fixed to some extent, because some pairs will play peacefully in two hearts or perhaps in one no trump. You must therefore double in an effort to get 300. Partner should regard this double as no more than a suggestion. He will not expect you to have much in diamonds, and if he does not fancy defending he can try for 140 by taking out to three hearts.

Game all. Dealer West

	West	North	East	South
♠ A 7 6 5	1 ♡	Double	2 ♡	2 ♠
♡ Q J 3	3 ♡	—	—	?
◇ 4 2				
♣ Q 8 6 3				

Contesting the Part-Score

Your side again seems to have the balance of power. You have defensive values in the enemy suit which would probably be useless in a spade contract, and a double therefore represents the safest way of trying for a better score.

5

Dummy Play

THE play of the hand in part-score contracts after a contested auction is one of the most interesting and rewarding fields of study in the pairs game. When opponents have been active in the bidding the evaluation of the contract takes on a new dimension.

In one minor way the problem is simplified, for you will seldom need to take a critical look at your choice of denomination. In a contested auction there is normally little choice—you just compete in your best suit. Against that must be set the complications caused by enemy action.

In close part-score situations it is inevitable that your side will be defending at some of the other tables. Before deciding on your trick target, therefore, you must consider how the opponents would have fared in the contract they were in, or might have been in.

Maintaining consistency between bidding and play is of vital importance on all competitive hands. In the bidding both sides will have made close decisions in the matter of passing, doubling, or bidding on. You must always assume that you have made the correct decisions and the enemy the wrong ones, however unlikely this may appear when dummy goes down. Start from the premise that you have reached, if not beaten, the par contract and back up your bidding in the play of the hand.

The opponents do not have to bid before you can envisage them playing the hand, of course. Often you will see that they could have made a part-score contract if obstructive action by you had not kept them out of the bidding.

Contesting the Part-Score

♠ Q 7 6 2
♡ A 8 3
◇ 10 6 3
♣ 10 8 4

Game all. Dealer South

	South	West	North	East
	1 NT	All pass		

♠ K 4
♡ K 6
◇ K Q J 8 5
♣ J 7 5 2

West leads the five of hearts against your one no trump contract. How should you plan the play?

Here you have a simple but typical match-point decision to take. Should you try to steal a spade trick in an effort to make your contract, or should you play on diamonds and settle for one down?

Not everyone will open one no trump with your hand. Anyone who plays in two diamonds will score plus 90, and you would need to make your contract to tie with that. But will there be anyone playing in two diamonds? West was unable to compete over your one no trump opening, but he might well be strong enough to put in a heart bid over an opening of one diamond. And it is crystal clear that the opponents could make eight or nine tricks in hearts for a score of 110 or 140.

Par on the hand, in other words, is represented by a contract of two or three hearts by West, and minus 100 for one down in one no trumps will be a par-beating score. What you cannot afford is minus 200. An attempt to steal a spade trick would therefore be too risky, for you could easily lose three hearts and three clubs and the aces of spades and diamonds.

You should therefore set yourself the modest target of six tricks on this hand. Win the first heart with dummy's ace and lead a diamond.

Dummy Play

♠ Q 9 8 5 3
♡ 7
◇ A J 7 6 2
♣ Q 3

Love all. Dealer West

	West	North	East	South
♠ 7 4	—	—	1 ♣	—
♡ K Q 9 2	1 ♡	Double	Redouble	1 NT
◇ 10 5 4	—	—	Double	All
♣ A J 6 2				pass

West leads the four of hearts to his partner's ace, and East returns the ten of hearts which you win with the king, discarding a spade from dummy. You lead the ten of diamonds on which West, after a momentary hesitation, plays the king. You play low in dummy, of course, and East follows with the three. West then switches to the nine of clubs, covered by the queen, king and ace. You lead another diamond and West plays the nine. What do you play from dummy?

On the bidding East is marked with a fairly balanced hand and he really should have the queen of diamonds. West's first-round hesitation very likely indicates that he started with the king and two other diamonds, in which case you can make an overtrick by dropping East's queen.

Is anyone tempted to go for the overtrick? No, of course not. In a doubled contract your job is to make the contract as safely as possible. Plus 180 will be a magnificent score, and you should not take the slightest risk to increase it to 280. Three diamond tricks are all you need for your contract and there is a sure way of making them. Just play a small diamond from dummy on the second round.

Perhaps you chose to finesse the knave, arguing that East could not bid like that with a singleton diamond. Well, don't look to me for sympathy if East shows out. Everyone does not bid like you, and it is losing tactics to trust the opponents' bidding when 100 per cent safety is available.

Contesting the Part-Score

♠ Q J 7 4
♡ 10 8 3
♢ 4 3
♣ K Q 8 2

Love all. Dealer West

West	North	East	South
♠ 6 2
♡ K 5
♢ K Q 10 9 7 5
♣ A 7 4

West	North	East	South
1 ♡	—	1 ♠	2 ♢
Double	All pass		

West leads the king of spades and continues with a small spade to his partner's ace. East returns the two of hearts and you play low. West takes the queen and cashes the ace, and you ruff East's knave on the third round. How should you continue?

You can count West for two spades and five hearts, and his remaining cards are probably four diamonds and two clubs. East would hardly have left the double in if void in diamonds. Even with a singleton his pass was dubious, for West could clearly have made about nine tricks in hearts.

Going one down in two diamonds should therefore be a good result, whereas two down will be a disaster. This means that you can afford to lose two trump tricks. Is there any danger of losing more? Yes, if you lead the king of diamonds now West will hold off. He will win the second round and force you with a heart lead, and you will have to lose three trumps in the end.

On this hand you must force West to win one of his trump tricks on the first round while there is still a trump in dummy to protect you from a heart force. You could achieve this by leading the ten of diamonds from hand, but there is added safety in crossing in clubs to lead the trump from dummy. This takes care of the chance that East's singleton is the knave when, in fact, you will make your contract.

The finesse of the nine or ten of diamonds on the first round is a safety play for one down, ensuring a good match-point score.

Dummy Play

♠ A 10 6 2
♡ 8 5
♢ 7 2
♣ J 10 8 7 3

Game all. Dealer South

♠ K 9 8 7 4
♡ 10 3
♢ A 9 4
♣ K Q 4

	South	West	North	East
	1 ♠	Double	3 ♠	—
	—	Double	All pass	

West starts off with the two top hearts against your doubled contract of three spades. He then switches to the king of diamonds, which you win with the ace. You lead a small trump to dummy's ace, West playing the knave and East the three, and return a trump on which East plays the five. Do you play the king or the seven from your hand?

This is a tricky decision to have to take with the contract depending on it. Plus 730 if you guess right and minus 200 if you guess wrong. The Rule of Restricted Choice tells you that the finesse is almost twice as likely to succeed as the drop, but here we are not concerned with probabilities and there is an overwhelming match-point argument in favour of playing for the drop.

Count your defensive tricks against a heart contract. You have a maximum of four—two spades, one diamond and one club. But you will make four tricks in defence only if the spades break 2–2. When the spades are 3–1 the opponents will be able to make game in hearts, and there is no reason why some pairs should not be in it. Minus 200 will be quite a respectable score when some pairs are losing 620. It will therefore be no tragedy to go one down when the trumps break 3–1.

It is when the trumps are 2–2 that you must at all costs make your contract. With no game on for the opponents, minus 200 will be very close to zero.

Contesting the Part-Score

♠ A 8 3
♡ K Q J 9 4
◇ A J 2
♣ 10 4

Love all. Dealer West

♠ 10 9 7 5 2
♡ 10 3
◇ 10 7 4
♣ K J 8

West	North	East	South
1 NT	Double	—	2 ♠
(12–14)			
All pass			

West leads the three of diamonds against your two spade contract. You play low from dummy, and East wins with the queen and returns the two of clubs. How should you play?

You must lose two spades, one heart and one diamond, and you can therefore afford to lose only one club. Before deciding on your play you should consider what is likely to happen in the alternative contract. After all, your decision to take out your partner's double was a border-line one, and some South players will probably choose to defend. If one no trumps doubled goes two down they will score 300 and you are destined to get a poor result whether you make two spades or not. You must keep faith with your bidding by assuming that West can make six tricks in no trumps, in which case plus 110 for making two spades will be a good score.

Playing in one no trumps West would need to develop the club suit. If the queen is with East he would lose two tricks in the suit which, with four hearts and two aces to lose as well, would put him two down.

You have to assume that he would go only one down and so you should play West for the queen of clubs and go up with your king on the second trick.

Dummy Play

♠ K 9 6 5
♡ J 9 7 4 3
♢ 8
♣ A J 4

East-West game. Dealer East

	West	North	East	South
♠ Q J 8 3			1 ♢	—
♡ K 10 2	—	Double	2 ♢	2 ♠
♢ K 10 6	—	—	3 ♢	—
♣ 8 7 5	—	3 ♠	—	—
	Double	All pass		

West leads the six of clubs against your doubled contract of three spades. You play the ace from dummy and East drops the king. On the lead of a small spade East plays the ace and leads the five of hearts. How should you play?

If East has led away from the queen you might be able to make this contract, but on the bidding West can hardly have the ace of hearts. In any case, if you go through the correct match-point motions and study your defensive potential it should be clear that you do not need nine tricks to score well on this hand. Against East's three-diamond contract you would not make more than one trick in each suit in defence. Not all North-South pairs will push up to the three-level in spades. A number of them will concede 110 defending against diamond contracts, and therefore minus 100 should give you a good score.

What you cannot afford is to go two down and lose 300, and that might happen if you play low and lose to a doubleton queen of hearts. You could even go three down if the enemy take a ruff in both hearts and clubs.

You should therefore make sure of eight tricks by playing the king of hearts on the first round. You can continue with the queen of spades, switching back to hearts if East shows out.

As you may have noticed, this is one of the hands from the previous chapter on bidding, switched through 180 degrees for convenience.

91

Contesting the Part-Score

♠ A 7 6 5
♡ A 9 6 3
♢ J
♣ A 9 8 4

North-South game. Dealer West

West	North	East	South
1 ◇	Double	1 NT	2 ♡
3 ◇	3 ♡	All pass	

♠ K J
♡ 10 8 7 4 2
♢ Q 10 3
♣ 6 5 2

West leads the ace of diamonds against your three heart contract, then switches to the king of clubs. How do you plan the play?

You are at an uncomfortably high level and you wish your partner had passed three diamonds, for it is immediately apparent that you have five certain tricks in defence. Minus 100 is sure to be a terrible score for you, so you simply cannot afford to go down in this contract. You must stand by your dubious bidding and assume that three hearts can be made.

You have just three losers in the minor suits, and at first glance it appears that you might get home if you lose only one trump trick. But remember the bidding. East would hardly bid one no trumps with a doubleton heart. He will surely have three hearts and that means that you have two inescapable trump losers.

Since you must make this contract you will have to get rid of one of your club losers. That means taking the spade finesse, even although it risks going two down. The proper sequence is: club ace, trump ace, spade to knave, spade king, diamond ruff, spade ace for club discard, spade ruff, and diamond ruff. That is eight tricks, and the three remaining trumps in your hand will be good for the ninth.

Dummy Play

♠ A Q 6 3
♡ Q 4
♢ A 9 6 4   *East-West game. Dealer East*
♣ J 9 3

	West	North	East	South
♠ 8			1 ♡	—
♡ K 10 2	2 ♡	Double	—	3 ♣
♢ 7 5 3	All pass			
♣ Q 10 8 7 5 2				

West leads the five of hearts against your three club contract. East wins and returns the king of diamonds to dummy's ace. How should you continue?

You have to decide between leading trumps and going quietly one off, or trying to make your contract by leading the queen of hearts to your king and taking the spade finesse. The latter method risks going two down if the spade finesse is wrong, of course.

Partner's double of two hearts will not be everyone's choice. Most of the North players will pass, and East-West will play in two hearts at a number of tables. The fate of the two heart contract is also likely to depend on the position of the spade king. The singleton spade is the obvious lead and if West has the king of spades the contract will go down, the defence taking two spade tricks, two spade ruffs, a trump trick and the ace of diamonds. If East has the king of spades, on the other hand, two hearts will be made.

Since you are not doubled in three clubs, the spade finesse offers you a unique two-way safety play, guaranteeing a good score whether the finesse wins or loses. When the finesse succeeds most North-Souths will score 100 for defeating two hearts, but you will top them with 110 for making three clubs. When the finesse fails, the other North-Souths will lose 110, but you will lose only 100 for two down in three clubs. It's a case of 'heads you win, tails they lose'.

Contesting the Part-Score

♠ K Q 8
♡ 10 9 7 4 3
◇ Q 7 3
♣ K 4

Love all. Dealer East

	West	North	East	South
♠ 10 3			1 ♠	—
♡ 5 2	2 ♠	—	—	2 NT
◇ A K 9 5	All pass			
♣ Q J 8 6 4				

You are still trying to recover from the shock of being left in two no trumps when West leads the four of spades and dummy goes down. Yes, partner has a point, you concede, but it is with some anxiety that you try the eight from dummy. All is well, for East plays the nine and your ten wins. You lead a small club and dummy's king is captured by the ace. East leads the ace and then the two of spades, and you discard a heart from hand. Both opponents follow when you lead a club to the knave, but on the next round East discards a heart. Now you try the diamonds, cashing the ace and leading low to the queen. Both opponents follow, West playing the ten on the second round. On the lead of dummy's third diamond East again plays small. How should you play?

Once again the Rule of Restricted Choice tells you that the finesse is a much superior play to the drop, and once again the match-point argument points in exactly the opposite direction. You are not interested in the best chance of making the contract: all you need is a good match-point score.

The sure way of getting a good score is to play for the drop. It is when the diamonds are 3–3 and two spades goes down that you must make certain of your two no trump contract. When the diamonds break 4–2 two spades will be made, and with other North-South pairs conceding 110 you will not mind registering minus 50 yourself.

Dummy Play

```
♠ Q J 10 8
♡ 9 7 4
◇ 10 6 3
♣ A 7 3
```

Love all. Dealer West

```
♠ A 9 6 5
♡ 10 2
◇ A J 9 4
♣ 8 6 5
```

	West	North	East	South
	1 ♡	—	1 NT	—
	2 ♡	—	—	2 ♠
	All pass			

Against your two spade contract West leads his fourth-highest heart—the knave. The comic continues with the queen and then the king. East discards the nine of clubs on the third round and you ruff. How should you continue?

In spite of the good trump support, dummy is a bit of a disappointment. You were entitled to expect rather more. The opponents must be very timid to have subsided at the two-level with all the stuff they hold.

Provided that East has the king of spades, as seems likely, you can always get out for one down, and it is very tempting to assume that minus 50 will be a good score. The trouble is that the enemy have altogether too much strength and it is likely that most East-West pairs will play in game. Four hearts will go one down on the natural spade lead, while three no trumps by East will be one or two down depending on the opening lead. To defeat the pairs who have a game bid against them, therefore, you will have to make this two spade contract.

The best chance of doing that lies in assuming West to have a doubleton diamond honour. To get the timing right you must lead the four of diamonds from hand at trick four. West will probably win and attack clubs, knocking out dummy's ace. You will now be able to finesse twice in spades and in diamonds, and if all goes well you will make nine tricks for a good score.

6

Defence

DEFENDING against part-score contracts is always a difficult business, but it is a little less hazardous when the defenders have been active in the bidding. At least one suit will have been mentioned, and there is a good chance that the defence will start off on the right lines.

Every bid or raise that your partner makes will carry some positive inference, and a number of negative inferences can always be gleaned from his failure to bid or raise. It is important to make full use of these in forming your estimate of his strength and distribution.

Reliable signalling and close partnership co-operation are needed to ensure that none of your defensive tricks run away. When you reflect that the difference between a good score and a poor one is often just one trick, it is clear how vital this matter is.

Your evaluation of the contract must, of course, be comprehensive, taking account of the likely score you would have received in your own contract as well as any alternative contract available to the declarer's side. In placing specific cards in your partner's hand, consider not only how they will affect the defence but also how they will affect the par for the hand. As always, in order to score well, you must keep faith with your bidding, assuming that your decision to pass or double was correct. If you made the wrong decision in the bidding there is not much hope for you, so you should refuse to entertain this possibility.

Defence

```
          ♠ 7 4
          ♡ K 9 3
          ◊ Q J 6 4          Love all
          ♣ A 9 6 5          Dealer South
♠ A J 8 3           South   West    North    East
♡ 4                 1 ♡     Double  Redouble  —
◊ A 10 8 3           —      1 ♠     2 ♡      All
♣ Q 10 7 4                                   pass
```

You lead the four of clubs against South's two heart contract and dummy's ace wins, partner playing the two and declarer the three. When the four of diamonds is led from the table your partner plays the seven and declarer the king. On taking your ace, how do you continue?

Discards on dummy's diamonds appear imminent, and it is tempting to switch to spades to make sure of all the tricks you can take in the suit plus any trump tricks partner may have.

A little counting will keep you right, however. Declarer can obtain at most two discards on the diamonds, and spade discards would help him only if he has fewer than four spades. Can partner have four spades including the king? Surely not, considering that he neither bid the suit over the redouble nor raised you.

Your spade tricks cannot run away, but club tricks might and you should therefore lead a club. If the full deal is as shown below you can actually beat the two heart contract.

```
          ♠ Q 6 5
          ♡ 10 8 5 2
          ◊ 9 7 5 2
          ♣ K 2
♠ K 10 9 2
♡ A Q J 7 6
◊ K
♣ J 8 3
```

Note that a spade switch would have presented declarer with no fewer than three extra tricks.

97

Contesting the Part-Score

				♠ Q 7 4 3
Love all				♡ —
Dealer East				◇ A 9 8 3
				♣ J 10 8 5 2

West	*North*	*East*	*South*	♠ K J 8 2
		1 NT	Double	♡ 9 4
—	2 ♣	—	2 ♡	◇ K Q J 6
2 ♠	Double	—	3 ♡	♣ Q 9 4
Double	All pass			

West leads the ten of diamonds against South's doubled contract of three hearts. Dummy plays low and so do you, and West continues with the two of diamonds which is won by the ace. The knave of clubs is led from dummy and when you play low South puts on the king, losing to your partner's ace. West leads the ten of spades and dummy plays low. Which card do you play?

A count tells you that South started with three diamonds, a singleton spade, probably no more than two clubs because of his play of the king, and therefore seven hearts. You have been lucky in that South misguessed the clubs, and you must not dissipate this luck by failing to give partner the guidance he needs now. The spade king is the proper card to play, for South's singleton may well be the ace. Partner is seeking your entry, and you must tell him there is no future in spades so that he will try a club when next he gets in.

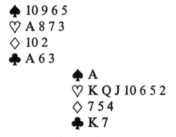

```
              ♠ 10 9 6 5
              ♡ A 8 7 3
              ◇ 10 2
              ♣ A 6 3
                        ♠ A
                        ♡ K Q J 10 6 5 2
                        ◇ 7 5 4
                        ♣ K 7
```

Plus 100 might not have been a bad result but plus 300 is better, especially when you can feel you have earned it.

Defence

```
                    ♠ J 9 4
Game all            ♡ 7 2
Dealer North        ◇ K J 8 3
                    ♣ A Q J 6
West   North  East  South      ♠ Q 10 8
       1 NT    —    2 ♣         ♡ K 9 5
2 ♡     —      —    3 ◇         ◇ A 4 2
All pass                       ♣ 10 7 5 3
```

West leads the ace of hearts and continues with the eight of hearts to your king, South following with the three and the knave. How do you plan the defence?

You have two tricks in the bag, and if partner has a spade honour you will be able to win two more tricks in that suit provided that you lead a spade at once.

But have you considered your own contract? Your partner clearly has six hearts and if he has a spade honour you have done the wrong thing already by not raising, because nine tricks in hearts can be made. Plus 100 for defeating three diamonds will be no use when other pairs are scoring 140 your way, so you must assume that partner's outside honour is the king of clubs. That means giving up hope of beating three diamonds and concentrating on preventing an overtrick.

Declarer's use of Stayman marks him with four spades and therefore no more than two clubs. Rather than rely on partner for the seven of spades, you should make sure of preventing a black suit squeeze by leading a club now. When in with the ace of diamonds, you can lead another club to break up the squeeze.

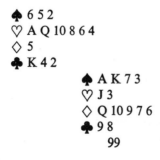

```
♠ 6 5 2
♡ A Q 10 8 6 4
◇ 5
♣ K 4 2
              ♠ A K 7 3
              ♡ J 3
              ◇ Q 10 9 7 6
              ♣ 9 8
```

Contesting the Part-Score

♠ Q 9 6 5 4
♡ 10 6 2   *Game all*
♢ Q J 10   *Dealer South*
♣ J 4

♠ A
♡ Q 9 5 3
♢ K 8 5 4
♣ A 7 6 2

	South	West	North	East
	1 ♠	Double	2 ♠	3 ♡
	3 ♠	All pass		

On your lead of the three of hearts East plays the king and declarer the ace. A low spade lead puts you in and you try to cash the queen of hearts, but South ruffs and leads another spade to dummy's queen, East following with the knave. The queen of diamonds is led from dummy, partner playing the six and the declarer the two, and you take your king. How should you continue?

Is it a cash-out situation where you have to grab your club tricks before they disappear? For a club switch to be right, partner will need to have the king and South will need to have four diamonds to enable him to discard one of dummy's clubs. But if that is the situation you would have at most three losers playing in hearts—one heart, one diamond and one club. It will do you no good to hold the declarer to nine tricks in spades if you have already slipped below par by not bidding four hearts.

Assume, therefore, that three spades is the par contract, which means that there is no need for haste over your club tricks. A passive heart or diamond return is indicated.

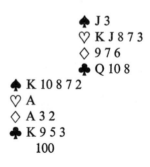

♠ J 3
♡ K J 8 7 3
♢ 9 7 6
♣ Q 10 8

♠ K 10 8 7 2
♡ A
♢ A 3 2
♣ K 9 5 3

100

Defence

♠ A 5
♡ K 10 9 6
◇ A 10 2
♣ K Q J 8

Love all
Dealer North

West	North	East	South	
	1 ♡	Double	1 ♠	♠ K Q
2 ◇	2 NT	Double	3 ♠	♡ A Q J
—	—		Double All pass	◇ Q J 7 4
				♣ A 10 6 2

Partner leads the three of diamonds. Declarer puts on the ace and leads out ace and another spade, partner echoing with the six and the three. How do you continue?

Clearly West has the diamond king, which means that your side could make eight tricks in no trumps and at least nine in diamonds. You will therefore need 300 for a good score.

From the opening lead and the trump echo you know that South has two diamonds and six spades, so he has five cards in hearts and clubs. If he has four clubs and one heart you will be unable to get him more than one down, but partner would surely have led a singleton club. South will not have four hearts on this bidding. If he has three hearts and two clubs you can get him two down by holding up your ace of clubs until the second round.

When South has two hearts and three clubs, however, you will need to give partner a club ruff, and this must be engineered before South can get back to his hand and draw the last trump. You should therefore lead the ten of clubs to lock the declarer in dummy. If partner echoes you will give him a ruff, otherwise you will just exit in diamonds and wait for your heart tricks.

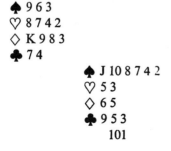

♠ 9 6 3
♡ 8 7 4 2
◇ K 9 8 3
♣ 7 4

♠ J 10 8 7 4 2
♡ 5 3
◇ 6 5
♣ 9 5 3

Contesting the Part-Score

```
           ♠ 6 5 4
           ♡ 4 3              Love all
           ◇ Q J 6 3         Dealer South
           ♣ Q J 10 6
♠ J 9 5               South   West   North   East
♡ A K J 9 6 2         1 NT    Double All pass
◇ 9 4                 (12–14)
♣ A 5
```

On your lead of the ace of hearts East plays the eight and South the five. How should you continue?

Presumably the eight is partner's highest heart and South has the queen guarded. East is sure to have an entry somewhere, so two hearts will be a make and you will need to get one no trumps two down to score well. This means that you cannot afford to give declarer a heart trick. Instead you must find partner's entry.

It is important to try suits in the right order. A diamond switch might take a finesse for the declarer, and it would clearly be risky to surrender control of the club suit. That leaves spades, but even here you must consider the best way to elicit partner's holding. If he has the ace there will be no problem, but he might have a lower honour or both king and queen. If you lead the three and partner's queen draws the declarer's ace, you will be in a quandary when you win declarer's club lead. To lead the knave is no better. Partner might have Q 8 7, and you will again be uncertain after taking your ace of clubs. The right card to lead is the nine of spades. Partner should not now play the queen unless he has the king as well. If East plays low on the spade lead and fails to encourage on the first round of clubs, you will switch to diamonds.

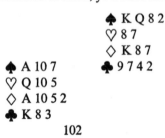

```
                    ♠ K Q 8 2
                    ♡ 8 7
                    ◇ K 8 7
              ♣ 9 7 4 2
♠ A 10 7
♡ Q 10 5
◇ A 10 5 2
♣ K 8 3
```

Defence

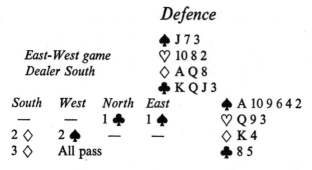

East-West game
Dealer South

♠ J 7 3
♡ 10 8 2
◇ A Q 8
♣ K Q J 3

South	West	North	East
—	—	1 ♣	1 ♠
2 ◇	2 ♠	—	—
3 ◇	All pass		

♠ A 10 9 6 4 2
♡ Q 9 3
◇ K 4
♣ 8 5

West leads the king and then the queen of spades. South follows both times, and West switches to the two of trumps. The eight is played from dummy and your king wins. How should you continue?

To give yourself any chance of defeating this contract you must clearly attack hearts before the declarer can get the clubs going. Partner is likely to have the ace of hearts, otherwise he would have led the suit himself in preference to trumps. If partner has the knave as well as the ace, you have a chance to get South two down by leading the queen. If South guesses wrong, playing you for both queen and knave, he may lose three heart tricks.

But before you lead that queen of hearts consider how your own contract would have gone. With the ace and knave of hearts in the West hand you would have only four losers in your spade contract. The assumption conflicts with your bidding and must therefore be thrown out. Replace the queen of hearts in your hand and try the nine instead. That's a good, deceptive card. Declarer will be suspicious, but he may come to the wrong conclusion and put up the king.

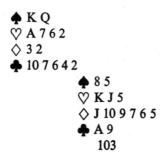

♠ K Q
♡ A 7 6 2
◇ 3 2
♣ 10 7 6 4 2

♠ 8 5
♡ K J 5
◇ J 10 9 7 6 5
♣ A 9

103

Contesting the Part-Score

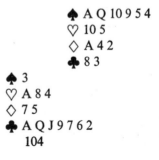

```
          ♠ 8 7 6 2
          ♡ Q 9 6 3        Game all
          ◇ K Q 8 6        Dealer East
          ♣ 4
♠ K J              West   North   East   South
♡ K J 7 2                          1 ♠    2 ♣
◇ J 10 9 3         2 ◇     —      2 ♠    3 ♣
♣ K 10 5           Double All pass
```

You lead the king of spades and partner overtakes with the
ace and continues with the queen. The declarer ruffs, cashes the
ace of clubs and follows with the queen of clubs which you win
with the king, East contributing the three and the eight of clubs.
How should you continue?

It doesn't look so good now, does it? Partner's failure to echo
means that South started with seven clubs, and he will also have
one of the red aces. To defeat this contract you will need to find
your partner's ace and get a spade lead through.

In a sense there is nothing to guide you, for partner has been
unable to signal to show where his entry lies. Nevertheless, there
is a very sound reason for leading a diamond.

Think of the possible contracts your way. If partner has the
ace of hearts three no trumps will be ice cold, and plus 200 will
not be much of a score when others are chalking up 600. But if
partner has the ace of diamonds, eight tricks will be the limit in
no trumps and nine tricks in spades, and your 200 will therefore
be a top. When there is a choice of plays it is only logical to pick
the one that will produce a good match-point score if it succeeds.

```
                    ♠ A Q 10 9 5 4
                    ♡ 10 5
                    ◇ A 4 2
                    ♣ 8 3
          ♠ 3
          ♡ A 8 4
          ◇ 7 5
          ♣ A Q J 9 7 6 2
```

104

Defence

				♠ K J
Game all				♡ 9 7 3
Dealer South				◇ A 8 7 6 3
				♣ Q J 4

South	West	North	East	♠ 8 7 4
—	—	1 ◇	—	♡ K Q 2
1 ♠	—	—	2 ◇	◇ Q 10 9 5 4
2 ♡	—	—	—	♣ A K

West leads the knave of diamonds against South's two heart contract, and the declarer plays low in dummy and ruffs in hand with the four of hearts. A spade is led to dummy's king and the knave of spades returned. Partner takes the ace and leads the five of trumps to your queen and the declarer's ace. South plays out the queen and then the ten of spades, and West follows both times while two clubs are thrown from dummy. How do you defend?

Declarer is marked with four cards in each major suit and therefore five clubs, and the bidding of both opponents seems like something from outer space. Nevertheless, it looks as though the enemy have succeeded in stealing your contract. If North had kept silent you would have opened one no trumps which would no doubt have been passed out. At other tables East might open one diamond and West bid one no trumps, or it might go one diamond, one spade, one no trumps. Certainly the final contract is likely to be one no trumps at most of the other tables, and it is all too clear that eight tricks can be made on any lead.

You will therefore need to defeat two hearts by two tricks in order to score well, and you will not do that if you ruff the fourth spade with the two of hearts and cash the king. No matter how you continue, the declarer will be able to score the ace of diamonds and a ruff in each hand.

It would be better to ruff with the king of hearts and return the two. This will defeat the contract by two tricks when partner has the knave of hearts, for he will continue with a third round of trumps to exhaust the suit. Unfortunately this defence will allow the declarer to make his contract when he has the knave of hearts, and while there will be little difference between plus 100 and minus 110 it could be worth a couple of match-points, which is not to be sneezed at.

The safe defence is to discard a diamond on the fourth spade. You will win the next lead and play king and another trump, and declarer will be one or two down depending on who has the knave of trumps.

The full hand:

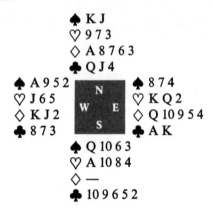

```
                    ♠ K J
                    ♡ 9 7 3
                    ◇ A 8 7 6 3
                    ♣ Q J 4
    ♠ A 9 5 2         N          ♠ 8 7 4
    ♡ J 6 5      W         E     ♡ K Q 2
    ◇ K J 2                      ◇ Q 10 9 5 4
    ♣ 8 7 3           S          ♣ A K
                    ♠ Q 10 6 3
                    ♡ A 10 8 4
                    ◇ —
                    ♣ 10 9 6 5 2
```

PART THREE

The Lead

7

Bidding

ON many boards the allocation of match-points between the defenders and the declarer is decided by the opening lead. Because of the match-point premium on overtricks, the lead is critical more often at pairs than at other forms of the game, and it follows that a good deal of attention should be paid in the bidding to the direction and inhibition of leads.

When bidding defensively—that is when you expect the opponents to win the declaration—the quality of your suit should play a big part in any decision you have to make. Remembering that partner is likely to lead the suit you call, you will need a powerful reason for bidding any suit which you would be unhappy to have led.

Light opening bids fall into the category of defensive bids, for there would clearly be no point in opening light if you did not fear that the opponents had the balance of power.

(a) ♠ 8 5	(b) ♠ 10 7 3
♡ A K Q J 6	♡ 9 4
◇ 10 7 6 3	◇ A K Q 9 8 3
♣ 5 2	♣ 7 6

The above hands are well worth an opening bid in first, second or third position. Apart from the competitive point of getting in the first blow, there is the big advantage of indicating a sound lead to your partner. If you pass on these hands, you may hear one spade on your left and four spades on your right. With nothing to guide him, partner may find the lead that concedes an overtrick.

The Lead

The position is very different when your high-card strength is not in your long suit.

(c) ♠ A 7
   ♡ Q 9 8 6 3
   ◇ K J 5 2
   ♣ 6 3

(d) ♠ A K J
   ♡ 9 4
   ◇ J 10 8 6 4 3
   ♣ 7 6

The above hands are sound passes in any position. There can be no advantage in opening sub-minimum hands where you have no particular wish for partner to lead your long suit.

Shaded third-in-hand bids should be made only in suits which you are prepared to have led.

(e) ♠ 9 3
   ♡ 10 9 7 5 2
   ◇ K Q J 5
   ♣ A 7

(f) ♠ J 10 6 3
   ♡ A Q J
   ◇ 7 4
   ♣ K 7 4 2

(g) ♠ K Q 10
   ♡ 9 5
   ◇ Q 8 7 6 3
   ♣ A 3 2

Nobody will force you to bid on any of the above hands, but if you feel inclined to have a go when third to speak the sensible bid is one diamond on (e), one heart on (f), and one spade on (g).

Some hands which qualify for a weak no trump opening are better opened with a suit bid when third in hand.

(h) ♠ K Q 10 2
   ♡ 9 6
   ◇ A J 7 4
   ♣ Q 6 3

(i) ♠ 8 7 3
   ♡ A Q J 2
   ◇ K 6
   ♣ Q 10 5 4

In first or second position you would open one no trumps on either of the above hands, but when third in hand it is better to bid one spade on (h) and one heart on (i), intending to pass partner's response. The loss of pre-emptive effect is slight, and if the opponents win the declaration you will at least have indicated a good lead.

Bidding

Responding

In responding to partner's opening bid there is one golden rule to bear in mind. With a weak hand, do not bid weak four-card suits.

(a) ♠ J 9 7 4
    ♡ 8 5
    ◇ K 7 2
    ♣ Q 9 4 3

(b) ♠ 5 2
    ♡ Q 9 7 6
    ◇ Q 6 3 2
    ♣ K 8 7

If partner opens one club your response on each of the above hands should be a raise to two clubs rather than a bid of the major suit. This may sound like heresy to some pairs players who have been taught never to miss the chance of finding a major suit fit. But there is no sound reason for straining to bid major suits on such hands. If partner has a strong hand he can always introduce his major suit over your raise to two clubs. If partner is weak the opponents are likely to get into the act, and on the above hands you do not wish to induce partner to lead from a doubleton honour in a major suit.

When you have a suit you are not ashamed of, or when your hand is stronger, it is another matter.

(c) ♠ K Q 10 4
    ♡ 9 7 6
    ◇ 10 4
    ♣ J 8 5 4

(d) ♠ 7 6
    ♡ A J 10 5
    ◇ J 9 5 2
    ♣ Q 4 2

(e) ♠ J 9 7 4
    ♡ 4 3 2
    ◇ A K 6
    ♣ K 8 7

By all means respond to partner's opening club bid with one spade on (c), since you can stand the lead of the suit. On (d) a response of one heart is preferable to the bookish approach bid of one diamond. On (e) a one-spade response is quite in order, since you have no intention of allowing the opponents to play the hand.

The Lead

Overcalls

The main reasons for overcalling are, of course, to contest the part-score or to prepare a sacrifice, but an important secondary function is to indicate a good lead. This does not mean that you should always refrain from overcalling when your suit is ragged or threadbare, but in border-line situations your ability to stand a lead in the suit should be the deciding factor.

(a)	♠ K 10 8 7	(b) ♠ Q 10 8 7
	♡ 8 6 5	♡ 8 6 5
	◇ 4	◇ 4
	♣ A 10 7 4 3	♣ A Q 7 4 3

If your left-hand opponent opens with a bid of one diamond, hand (a) is just about worth a non-vulnerable overcall of one spade. You have the master suit, the overcall removes enemy bidding space, and a spade lead from partner may be useful in defence. On hand (b) the desirability of a spade lead is doubtful (you wouldn't want partner to lead the ace from ace and another, for instance) and this should just tip the balance against overcalling.

At times it may be worth while overcalling for the sole purpose of directing a lead.

♠ 10 6 2
♡ 7 5 4
◇ K Q J 6
♣ 10 9 2

East-West game. Dealer East

West	North	East	South
		1 ♣	?

Here there is little prospect of contesting the part-score and you cannot envisage a sacrifice against an enemy game, yet a diamond lead from partner against a no trump contract (or any contract, for that matter) might be worth quite a lot of match-points to you. An overcall of one diamond on such a hand can also have an inhibiting effect on the opponents. The full deal might be as follows.

Bidding

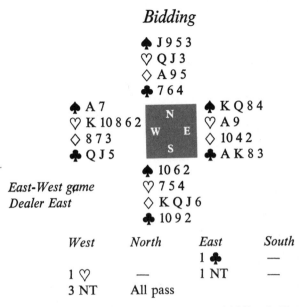

```
              ♠ J 9 5 3
              ♡ Q J 3
              ◇ A 9 5
              ♣ 7 6 4
    ♠ A 7          N          ♠ K Q 8 4
    ♡ K 10 8 6 2   W   E      ♡ A 9
    ◇ 8 7 3            S      ◇ 10 4 2
    ♣ Q J 5                   ♣ A K 8 3
              ♠ 10 6 2
              ♡ 7 5 4
              ◇ K Q J 6
              ♣ 10 9 2
```

East-West game
Dealer East

West	North	East	South
		1 ♣	—
1 ♡	—	1 NT	—
3 NT	All pass		

If you leave the opponents in peace the bidding is likely to proceed as shown above. But if you insert a cheeky overcall of one diamond it will be very hard for the enemy to get there. Unsure of the diamond position, they may well finish up in an unmakable four heart contract.

When both opponents are bidding it is dangerous to overcall, but at pairs it can be even more dangerous to pass.

```
♠ A Q J 6 2
♡ 7 3          East-West game. Dealer West
◇ 8 6 3        West   North   East   South
♣ 7 6 5        1 ♣    —       1 ♡    ?
```

Since partner could not bid over one club there is not likely to be anything on for your side. Nevertheless, you should certainly put in an overcall of one spade to indicate a defence. Even at game all the risk would be worth taking, but at adverse vulnerability the danger would outweigh the advantage for the opponents would double you at the slightest provocation.

The Lead

♠ 6 5 3
♡ K 6
◇ 7 4 2
♣ K Q J 9 3

	East-West game. Dealer South		
South	*West*	*North*	*East*
—	1 ◇	—	1 ♡
?			

This will be your last chance to tell your partner that you want a club rather than a spade lead against a no trump contract. The advantage of a two club overcall outweighs the risk involved.

Responding to Overcalls

Here again there are opportunities for indicating a good lead, and at pairs there is always an incentive to go out of your way to do so.

♠ 9 8 6 3
♡ 8 6
◇ A Q J 6 4
♣ 8 2

	East-West game. Dealer West		
West	*North*	*East*	*South*
1 ♡	1 ♠	2 ♣	?

The opponents would appear to have the balance of strength, but you should be prepared to contest up to the three-level in spades.

The best immediate bid is two diamonds. You are unlikely to be left to play in this contract and it will be no tragedy if you are. But you will probably get a chance to show your spade support at a later stage. The diamond bid will help your partner to decide whether or not to sacrifice over four hearts, and if he decides to defend he will get off to the right start.

♠ 7 3
♡ 9 8
◇ 10 9 8 5 2
♣ K J 6 4

	Game all. Dealer West		
West	*North*	*East*	*South*
1 ♡	Double	Redouble	?

The opponents clearly have the balance of power, but with a five-card suit you are probably not too worried. Your bid should be two clubs, however, not two diamonds. The enemy will probably finish in a heart contract, and the initial lead of a club from your partner could make a difference of a number of match-points. The complete hand might be as follows.

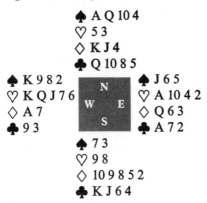

```
                    ♠ A Q 10 4
                    ♡ 5 3
                    ◇ K J 4
                    ♣ Q 10 8 5
    ♠ K 9 8 2                    ♠ J 6 5
    ♡ K Q J 7 6      N           ♡ A 10 4 2
    ◇ A 7         W     E        ◇ Q 6 3
    ♣ 9 3            S           ♣ A 7 2
                    ♠ 7 3
                    ♡ 9 8
                    ◇ 10 9 8 5 2
                    ♣ K J 6 4
```

A bid of two diamonds from you would very likely induce a diamond lead from your partner, and that would permit West to make ten tricks.

Lead-Directing Doubles

The commonest of these is the double of an enemy three no trump contract. When either you or your partner has mentioned a suit, the double asks for the lead of that suit. If you have both bid suits the double asks for the doubler's suit to be led. When neither defender has bid the double requests a lead through dummy's first-bid suit and, finally, when the opponents have mentioned no suits the double asks partner to lead his shorter major suit.

Such doubles are of most value at team or rubber bridge. At pairs they should be used with great discretion. For the double to be a worth-while proposition you must be practically certain that the lead you direct will defeat the contract. If the declarer manages to put together nine tricks in spite of the lead you will get a bottom score even when other declarers are making undoubled

The Lead

overtricks. When there is any doubt at all it is better to pass and hope that partner will find the lead on his own.

What looks like a sure thing may turn out to be anything but sure in the event. Here is a hand on which I managed to convert a top into a bottom.

♠ Q J 2		*Love all. Dealer West*		
♡ 6 3	*West*	*North*	*East*	*South*
◇ K Q J 10 9 3	1 NT	—	2 ♣	2 ◇
♣ A 8	—	—	3 NT	?

It seemed to me that the declarer could make a maximum of seven tricks—two spades, four hearts and the diamond ace—and so I doubled to make sure of the lead. I quickly regretted it, for the full hand was as shown below.

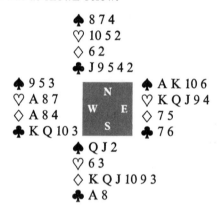

Partner had a diamond all right, but I had failed to allow for East's erratic bidding. West won the second diamond lead and ran the hearts. I discarded the two of spades, the eight of clubs and the ten of diamonds, but the declarer read the position correctly and dropped my spade honours to make an overtrick.

All the other East-West pairs played in four hearts making ten tricks. Had I passed the three no trump bid my partner would still have led a diamond and I could have played safe for four defensive tricks and a top score.

Bidding

When it comes to slam doubles the picture is rather different. In pairs as in other forms of the game, the Lightner slam double asking for an unusual lead is a valuable tool. Any slam made against you is likely to give you a poor score, and therefore doubling for a lead stands to gain much more than it can lose.

♠ 8 3		*Love all. Dealer North*		
♡ 9 7 6 2	*West*	*North*	*East*	*South*
◇ —		—	1 ◇	2 ♣
♣ K Q 10 8 6 5 2	2 ♠	—	3 ♠	—
	4 NT	—	5 ♡	—
	6 ♠	—	—	?

You will get few match-points if six spades is made against you, and on balance it will pay to double for a diamond lead and take your chance on being able to pick up another trick somewhere. Since West elected to play in spades there is no reason to think he can make a successful conversion to six no trumps.

Enemy trial bids and cue bids offer opportunities which should be seized with both hands.

♠ 9 8 4 3		*Game all. Dealer West*		
♡ 5 2	*West*	*North*	*East*	*South*
◇ K J 10 8 4	1 ♠	—	2 ♣	—
♣ 10 4	2 ♡	—	3 ◇	?

East may or may not have a genuine diamond suit, but there is little risk in doubling. Your diamond holding is strong enough to make a redouble unlikely. A diamond lead from your partner may not defeat the final contract, but it is certainly likely to keep the overtricks down.

The Blackwood Slam Convention is one of the most abused of all bidding tools. When the bidding reaches the required level many players automatically press the Blackwood button for the pleasure of seeing the wheels go round. This gives alert defenders some good opportunities for making lead-directing doubles.

The Lead

Love all. Dealer West

	West	North	East	South
♠ 8 7	West	North	East	South
♡ K Q 5 4	1 ♠	—	3 ♣	—
◇ 10 8 7 3	3 ♠	—	4 ♠	—
♣ K 6 2	4 NT	—	5 ♡	?

The double is marked. It will not succeed every time, but on balance it is sure to pay. No less useful are the negative inferences to be obtained when your partner fails to double a Blackwood response or other high-level cue bid.

Lead-Directing Cue Bids

In competitive auctions when you have agreed a suit with partner there is little point in introducing a further suit except in order to tell him what to lead.

	West	North	East	South
♠ 7	*Game all. Dealer West*			
♡ A Q J 8 7 6 2	West	North	East	South
◇ K Q J 10 3	1 ♠	—	3 ♠	4 ♡
♣ —	4 ♠	5 ♡	5 ♠	?

Perhaps you will be tempted to bid six diamonds at this point, intending to make a Lightner double to ask for a club lead if West goes on to six spades.

The flaw in this reasoning is that partner might double ahead of you and lead a diamond. There is no need for you to complicate the issue by bidding diamonds at all. The lead you want against a spade slam is a club, and you should therefore bid six clubs over East's five spades.

Opportunities for lead-direction are often missed in competitive situations where the opponents seem likely to sacrifice against your game contract.

	South	West	North	East
♠ A 6	*Love all. Dealer South*			
♡ 10 9 7 5 4 2	South	West	North	East
◇ 3	1 ♡	1 ♠	3 ♡	3 ♠
♣ A K 9 5	?			

Bidding

Of course you are worth four hearts, but you have to think about what will follow. West will probably go on to four spades, and if you decide to defend against that contract you will need to obtain a diamond ruff to exact the maximum penalty. This way to preserve all your chances is to bid four clubs at this point. This should help your partner to decide whether or not to contest further over four spades. If partner passes four spades you will double, win the club lead, and return your diamond.

The full hand:

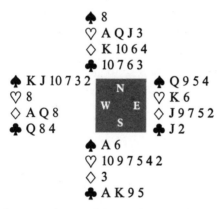

```
                      ♠ 8
                      ♡ A Q J 3
                      ◇ K 10 6 4
                      ♣ 10 7 6 3
    ♠ K J 10 7 3 2          ♠ Q 9 5 4
    ♡ 8              N      ♡ K 6
    ◇ A Q 8      W       E  ◇ J 9 7 5 2
    ♣ Q 8 4          S      ♣ J 2
                      ♠ A 6
                      ♡ 10 9 7 5 4 2
                      ◇ 3
                      ♣ A K 9 5
```

Double-dummy, eleven tricks can be made in hearts against any lead except a trump, but in practice South is likely to make only ten.

Obstructive Tactics

When the opponents do not enter the bidding we see the opposite side of the medal. Now it is the enemy who will have to make the opening lead, and your aim should be to assist their choice as little as possible.

There is inevitable conflict between the twin objectives of bidding. You are anxious to make the best of your own cards, but at the same time you are reluctant to allow the enemy to make the best of theirs. Often it is necessary to choose between a con-

The Lead

structive bid which will give partner precise information to help in his assessment of the final resting place, or an obstructive bid which will sacrifice some accuracy in order to withhold information from the opponents. It is usually best, especially at pairs, to choose the obstructive bid.

In a rubber or team game the opening lead will be critical on perhaps one deal in five, when the right choice of lead can result in the defeat of the contract. At pairs, on the other hand, the opening lead is critical whenever the choice of lead may make the difference of a trick—on every other deal perhaps. Thus a straightforward, intentionally blunt style of bidding is more likely to pay dividends than a slow, scientific approach.

Limit bids and quantitative raises give little away and should usually be preferred to subtle approach bids. One of the merits of the weak no trump is that it frequently makes possible the auction 1 NT–3 NT, leaving the opening leader with little to guide him but the thirteen cards in front of his nose. How much more informative is an auction like:

South	North
1 ♠	2 ♣
2 ♢	3 ♠
3 NT	—

West might, of course, have an automatic lead which he would make against either auction. But he might also have a choice of leads, in which case he is much more likely to produce the killer against the second auction than against the first.

I am not suggesting that all hands should be bid without the aid of science. Inevitably there are hands that require detailed investigation before you can decide on the best contract, and on those you must use whatever machinery you have available and take your chance on helping the defenders in the process. But whenever you have a good idea of what the final contract ought to be, you should bid it without further messing about. A slight reduction in the chance of reaching the par contract is well worth accepting for the chance of beating par on the lead.

Bidding

♠ K Q 10 4	*Love all. Dealer South*	
♡ Q 2	*South*	*North*
◇ A K 6	1 ♣	1 ♡
♣ A J 9 5	?	

To investigate the full possibilities of the hand there can be no doubt that two spades is the best rebid. But I am convinced that the winning bid, particularly at pairs, is a direct jump to three no trumps. The times when you miss a superior spade contract will be more than balanced by the occasions when you receive a spade lead in three no trumps.

Bidding, after all, is no more than an estimation of probabilities. There is no guarantee that the slow approach will reach a better contract than the direct game bid. Anyone who seeks complete bidding accuracy on every hand is akin to those who dream of perpetual-motion machines.

♠ K Q J 9 4	*Game all. Dealer South*	
♡ 6	*South*	*North*
◇ A Q 9 7 6	1 ♠	2 NT
♣ Q J	?	

Here there could be a slam only if partner has precisely the right cards, and the chance is too remote to make it worth looking into. Don't tip your hand with a three diamond bid. Just say four spades. Apart from the chance of a diamond lead, concealing your distribution may turn out to be worth a trick in the play.

♠ A Q 10 6 3	*Game all. Dealer South*	
♡ K Q 3	*South*	*North*
◇ A J 7 5	1 ♠	2 ♡
♣ 7	?	

I trust that no reader who is still with me would give West the opportunity to double a three diamond bid. The obvious and correct bid is a quantitative raise to four hearts. If partner is slam-minded he can make a try himself.

The Lead

One final example:

♠ A Q 10 6	*Game all. Dealer South*	
♡ A Q 10 7 3	*South*	*North*
◇ A K 8	1 ♡	3 ♡
♣ 2	?	

If partner has the values for his limit raise there is sure to be a reasonable play for twelve tricks. At worst it will depend on a finesse. A grand slam, however, is so unlikely that it is not worth considering, and so there is no point in picking daisies on the way up. Just bid six direct and keep the opponents guessing about your distribution.

8

Dummy Play

AFTER playing a hand for all it is worth to make an overtrick in a three no trump contract, it is disconcerting to open the travelling score slip and see that some other declarers have made a trick more than you. Although it does not help your score, it is a sop to your self-esteem when you see that they received a more helpful lead. 'They got a diamond lead,' you tell your partner bitterly. 'Any idiot could make eleven on a diamond lead.'

The luck of the lead (luck as far as the declarer is concerned, although it may be a matter of good or bad judgement on the part of the defender on lead) plays a critical role in every other deal. It is a factor that should be taken into account in your initial appraisal of the contract, and it should often influence your line of play.

Sometimes you will receive a helpful lead which gives you a trick you could not otherwise have made. This will incline you towards safety in the play of the hand. At pairs it will not often be right to aim for complete safety, but you will tend to avoid risky plays for overtricks when you already have an overtrick in the bag.

At other times the enemy will produce a deadly lead. If you judge that most of the other declarers will be luckier, you will need to take risks in an effort to recover. Do not resign yourself to an unlucky board. Look for some means of fighting back and you will be surprised how often you find a way.

The Lead

♠ A 6
♡ K 7 3
◇ K 10 6 5 3
♣ K 9 5

Love all
Dealer South

South	North
1 NT	3 NT

♠ 10 5
♡ A Q 4
◇ Q 7
♣ A 10 8 6 3 2

West leads the ten of hearts against your three no trump contract. How do you plan the play?

It is lucky for you that West didn't find the spade lead. At many of the other tables North is likely to be the declarer and a spade will be led. The contract will then go down if a club trick has to be lost. Should you then make sure of nine tricks by safety-playing the clubs? You can guard against four clubs in either hand by finessing the eight or nine of clubs at the second trick.

That play would be correct at team or rubber bridge, but it is out of the question at pairs. It gains only when the clubs are 4–0 and gives up all chance of more than nine tricks in the 90 per cent zone where clubs break 2–2 or 3–1. Remember that the declarers who receive a spade lead will have no option but to try to bring in the club suit without loss, and if they succeed they will make ten tricks. The favourable lead has given you a good chance of eleven tricks and you must not pass it up.

The only concession you can make to safety is to win the first trick in dummy and lead a small club from the table. Presumably East has length in spades and is therefore more likely to be short in clubs. By leading the first club through him you will be able to deal with the situation where he is void. If East plays small you should play the ace and return a club to the king. And if East plays an honour on the first round you can give yourself the best chance of six club tricks by finessing the nine on the way back.

Dummy Play

```
♠ 8 7 2
♡ A K J 10 3
♢ 7 4                          Game all
♣ 10 8 2                     Dealer South
                             South    North
♠ K Q 10 4                   1 ♣      1 ♡
♡ Q 2                        3 NT     —
♢ A K 6
♣ A J 9 5
```

Perhaps you remember the South hand from the last chapter. On this occasion the jump to game has the desired effect, for West leads the three of spades against your three no trump contract. East wins with the ace and returns the two of diamonds. How do you plan the play?

The diamond switch is not so friendly, but you are still a tempo ahead of the declarers who bid spades and receive an initial diamond lead. Those declarers will run the heart suit and then lead a spade from dummy. Finding the ace favourably placed, they will probably make ten tricks.

You could, of course, settle for the same ten safe tricks, but this would be cowardly when you are favourably placed to try for eleven. The proper play is to make use of both heart entries in dummy in order to finesse in clubs. The odds of three to one in favour of this play should be good enough for anyone.

A further point to consider is that some pairs might play in four hearts. In that contract they are likely to make eleven tricks unless the clubs lie badly. You will therefore need eleven tricks in no trumps to outscore anyone playing in hearts.

The Lead

♠ K Q 3		
♡ Q J 4		
◇ A J 9 7	*Game all*	
♣ A Q 5	*Dealer North*	
	North	*South*
♠ 7	1 ◇	1 ♡
♡ A K 10 5	3 NT	4 ◇
◇ K 10 6 2	4 ♡	—
♣ J 4 3 2		

West leads the ten of spades and dummy's queen is taken by the ace. East returns the five of spades, you throw a club from hand, and West's nine forces the king. You draw trumps with some trepidation, but to your relief the suit breaks 3–3. How should you continue?

Clearly you are not in the normal contract here. It would have been better if partner had signed off in four no trumps over your four diamond bid. Or perhaps you should have reverted to no trumps yourself. Be that as it may, North is likely to play in a no trump contract at most other tables.

The lead seems fairly certain to be the five of spades from East, and it is easy enough to forecast how the play will go. The declarers will finesse diamonds into the East hand to protect their spade holding, and they will make ten or eleven tricks depending on whether or not the finesse wins. They might even make twelve if they find West with a doubleton king of clubs. Since you have been lucky enough to get an even trump break you may score the same number of tricks by the same play, but this will be worth no match-points.

To outscore the no trump declarers you must make a trick more than them. The only way to do this is to play East for the queen of diamonds and take the finesse the other way. If your luck is in this may convert a bottom into a top.

Dummy Play

♠ K 6 4
♡ A J 10
◇ 9 7 3
♣ A Q 6 2

♠ A Q 7 5 2
♡ 3
◇ Q J 10 4
♣ 8 7 3

East-West game
Dealer North

North	South
1 NT	2 ♠
—	

Against your two spade contract West leads the king of diamonds and East plays the eight. West continues with the two of
diamonds to his partner's ace and ruffs the third round with the
three of spades. He then switches to the four of clubs. How do you
plan the play?

That was a diabolical lead of the king from king and another.
The contract of two spades is likely to be the standard one, but it
is a safe bet that no other declarer will suffer a diamond ruff. Is
there any way of recovering?

On a normal trump break the declarers in two spades will make
nine or ten tricks depending on the club finesse. For you to make
nine tricks by taking the club finesse would give you a zero.
When the club finesse is wrong you will still be close to zero,
beating only any optimist who plays in four spades. The only
hope of scoring on this hand is to play for East to have a doubleton
king of clubs.

You should therefore play the ace of clubs and draw trumps.
Of course if West proves to have had four trumps originally the
diamond ruff has cost you nothing, so you can play West for the
king of clubs after all. But if, as is more likely, the trumps were
3–2 originally you should continue by leading a club and ducking
in dummy. If you are lucky enough to find East with a doubleton
king this should pull your score back to average on the board.

127

The Lead

♠ A Q J 2
♡ Q J 10 5
◇ 9 6 4 2
♣ 7

Game all
Dealer South

South	North
1 ♠	3 ♠
4 ♠	—

♠ 10 9 8 5 4 3
♡ —
◇ A 8 3
♣ A K 8 5

West leads the two of clubs against your four spade contract and you capture East's knave with your ace. How should you continue?

That lead doesn't do you any harm. Those who receive a diamond lead will have nothing to do but try the trump finesse. They will make ten tricks if it fails and eleven (with a slight chance of twelve) if it succeeds. If you take a losing trump finesse you will be held to ten tricks as well, for East will certainly switch to diamonds. On the other hand you can be fairly sure of eleven tricks if you play the ace of trumps on the first round and run the queen of hearts for a diamond discard. West can hardly have both ace and king of hearts or he would have led the suit, and so you will be able to establish a heart winner for a diamond discard.

However, it would be annoying to adopt this method and later discover that the trump finesse was right and you could have made twelve tricks.

You can, in fact, improve your chances by leaving the trumps alone for the meantime. Ruff a club at trick two and run the queen of hearts. If West wins and finds the diamond switch, ruff another club and run the knave of hearts. If East covers you will have to abandon the trump finesse and make sure of your diamond discard, but you will at least have given both opponents a chance of going wrong. And you will be sure of making the maximum number of tricks when East has both ace and king of hearts.

Dummy Play

♠ A K 6
♡ 9 3
♢ K 8   *Love all*
♣ A Q J 7 6 3   *Dealer South*

	South	North
♠ J 5 2	—	1 ♣
♡ A 10 2	2 NT	3 NT
♢ A Q 10 4		
♣ 10 9 5		

West leads the six of hearts against your three no trump contract and East plays the queen. How do you plan the play?

The contract is normal but the lead unfavourable. In a rubber or team game this would not worry you very much. You would just hold up your ace until the third round, and then make ten or eleven tricks depending on the success of the club finesse.

But at pairs you cannot afford to settle for eleven tricks when twelve may be there for the taking, so the hold-up for two rounds is out of the question. What about holding up once and winning the second round of hearts, then? That would provide safety when West started with six hearts, yet would still allow you to make twelve tricks when the club finesse is right.

Like most compromise solutions, this is not very satisfactory. The modicum of safety provided does not compensate in full for the loss of the chance of making a thirteenth trick. If the club finesse is right this is a distinct possibility. The knave of diamonds or the queen of spades could drop, or there might be a squeeze.

You are fixed to some extent by the opening lead. Anyone who receives a different lead is sure to beat you when the club finesse is wrong. Your only chance of sharing the match-points with them is to assume the club finesse to be right and go for the maximum by winning the first trick.

The Lead

♠ A 10 4
♡ J 5 3
◇ K 5 4
♣ 10 6 4 2

Love all. Dealer South

South	West	North	East

♠ K 9 2
♡ 10 8 6 4
◇ A 7
♣ A J 5 3

South	West	North	East
1 NT	All pass		

West leads the five of spades against your one no trump contract and you capture East's queen with your king. How should you continue?

The spade lead appears to have given you a present of a trick you could not otherwise have made. Assuming that the finesse of the spade ten will succeed, you have three spade tricks and two diamonds, and you can make certain of two club tricks by making the safety play of the ace of clubs first.

Should you play it like that? No, of course not. Not in the pairs game. The distribution catered for by the safety play—a singleton honour in either hand—is too unlikely to warrant consideration, and there is quite a good chance of making three club tricks.

Remember that one no trumps might be played by the North hand at some tables. Anyone who receives a diamond lead will have no option but to try for three club tricks, and you should aim to beat those pairs, not just tie with them.

The best way to try for three club tricks is to lead a small club from hand at trick two, playing West for a doubleton honour in the suit. This is quite likely since West appears to have length in spades. And even if you have to lose two club tricks you will still make your contract, for by this method you retain your double stopper in both spades and diamonds.

Dummy Play

♠ A J
♡ J 8 6 4 3
♢ A K J 4   *Game all*
♣ A J   *Dealer North*

	North	South
♠ 10 6 3	2 NT	3 ♡
♡ A 9 7 5 2	4 ♡	—
♢ 7		
♣ 10 5 3 2		

West leads the eight of spades against your four heart contract. How should you plan the play?

You look like losing a spade and a club. If there is only one trump loser you will make your contract for a score of 620, but this will bring in very few match-points.

Reflect for a moment on your partner's choice of opening bid. Two no trumps on that hand is a little eccentric and you can be sure it will not be the popular choice. Most of the North players will open one heart and eventually play in the heart game from the other side of the table. Unfortunately you can see that it doesn't much matter what lead they get. Any side suit lead will enable them to make eleven tricks in comfort, and even a trump lead will permit them to try for the eleventh trick without risk by finessing in diamonds.

Since the lead through dummy's spade holding has put you at a disadvantage, you must risk the contract in an attempt to recover. The only chance is to win the first trick with the ace of spades, enter your hand with the ace of trumps, and lead a diamond for a finesse of the knave. If the finesse fails you will lose four tricks and get a zero, but you were doomed to something like a zero even if you made ten tricks. If the finesse succeeds, however, you will get your losing spades away on the ace and king of diamonds and break even on the board.

The Lead

```
♠ K 6 4
♡ A K Q 10 9
♦ 6 3                        Love all
♣ J 7 2                   Dealer South
                        South    North
♠ A J                    1 NT     3 ♡
♡ 7 2                    3 NT      —
♦ A K 5 4
♣ 10 8 6 5 3
```

West leads the two of spades against your three no trump contract and you take East's ten with your knave. How should you continue?

Since West appears to have led from the queen of spades, the lead has given you a present of a trick. Anyone who gets a diamond lead, or an initial spade lead from East, will require five heart tricks to make three no trumps, while you need only four.

There are two methods of trying for five heart tricks, one of which is slightly superior to the other. To take a first-round finesse gives you a straight fifty-fifty chance, succeeding whenever West has the knave. To play for the drop in hearts succeeds when the suit breaks 3–3 or when the knave is singleton or doubleton, which adds up to a total chance of about 54 per cent.

Those who do not receive a gift of a spade trick will go with the odds by adopting the second method, and they will make nine tricks just over half the time. By adopting the other method you can guarantee your contract all the time and still have a 50 per cent chance of an overtrick.

Cash the ace of spades to avoid any blockage, therefore, and then finesse the nine of hearts.

Dummy Play

♠ J 10 7 5 2
♡ J 10 5
◇ Q 4
♣ K 7 2

Game all
Dealer South

	South	North
	1 ♡	2 ♡

♠ 4
♡ K Q 9 6 3
◇ K 7 5
♣ A J 10 8

West leads the four of trumps against your two heart contract and East follows with the eight. You win in hand and lead a diamond to dummy's queen. East produces the ace and returns a heart, and West takes the ace and continues with a third round of trumps. How do you plan the play?

Those trump leads were far from friendly. By preventing you from ruffing a diamond in dummy the defenders have, in effect, stolen one of your tricks. It is unlikely that this defence will be duplicated at many of the other tables. Most pairs will play in two hearts all right, but they will lose a maximum of one trick in each suit. The natural way for them to play the clubs will be to take a first-round finesse against East after ruffing the diamond in dummy. If the finesse succeeds they will make ten tricks, and you have no hope of equalling that.

You must therefore assume that the natural club finesse will fail, in which case the other declarers will make only nine tricks. You may also be able to make nine tricks by taking the club finesse the other way—through West. Unless the club nine drops you will need a 3–3 break in the suit as well, which reduces the chance of success, but there is nothing else to try.

9

Defence

THE study of the defensive aspects of the opening lead divides itself naturally into two parts. One concerns the choice of lead itself, and the other the effect of the lead on subsequent play. The first part is very much more important for it will not often be possible to recover if the initial lead turns out poorly.

Bearing in mind that the object of defence at pairs is not necessarily to defeat the contract, the opening leader has to modify his tactics. What is the best lead in a team game may be quite wrong at pairs.

In general the tendency should be towards conservatism. Desperation leads and flights of fancy should be shunned, unless your position is such that you must get tops. Ideally, you should try to find a lead that will not give away a trick. If this is not possible, the next best thing is to try to choose the lead that everyone else will make. Whether this lead gives away a trick or not it will keep you nicely in the middle of the field, which is where you want to be.

The best lead against a three no trump contract, as a famous authority once remarked, is the ace from A K Q J 10. Certainly the opening leader will have no problem when he has any sort of solid sequence. The combination of aggression with safety makes the lead from a sequence an obvious and ideal choice. When you have a balanced hand, the top card of a much less dynamic sequence will usually prove to be a better choice than a lead from a tenace holding.

Defence

<pre>
♠ K 10 4 2
♥ 7 4   South   North
♦ 10 9 8 6   1 ♥   2 ♣
♣ A 9 5   2 NT   3 NT
</pre>

On balance the lead of the ten of diamonds will turn out best. A spade lead is too likely to cost a trick. The quest for safety should not be overdone, however.

<pre>
♠ K 10 4 3 2
♥ 7 4   South   North
♦ 10 9 8 6   1 ♥   2 ♣
♣ A 9   2 NT   3 NT
</pre>

Again the spade lead is more likely to give away a trick than the diamond, but now there is a better chance of establishing spade tricks for the defence. The fifth card tips the balance in favour of the spade lead.

When the hands are balanced all round the table a passive lead may well be best. This is often the case when the enemy probe for a suit fit before settling in no trumps.

<pre>
♠ K J 6 3   South   North
♥ 9 8 4   1 NT   2 ♣
♦ Q 7   2 ♦   2 NT
♣ A 9 5 2   —
</pre>

No lead is particularly attractive here, but the nine of hearts is least likely to give away a trick. Another occasion for a short suit lead is when your hand is so weak that there is little chance of setting up your own suit.

<pre>
♠ 8 5
♥ K 7   South   North
♦ 10 8 6 3   1 ♥   2 ♦
♣ 9 7 6 4 2   2 NT   3 NT
</pre>

A club lead is unlikely to be productive of many tricks. The better shot is the eight of spades. With any luck you may hit your partner's length.

The Lead

But on most hands an attacking lead from your long suit will give the best chance, even when you have only four card length. When the opponents have long suits to establish it is important not to waste the tempo of the opening lead. You must use it to try and set up your own suit first. In choosing between four card suits, preference should be given to the suit containing two honour cards or a bit of extra stuffing.

♠ J 7 2		
♡ Q 10 7 4	*South*	*North*
◇ K 3	1 ◇	1 ♠
♣ K 8 6 5	1 NT	—

The four of hearts is likely to prove to be the best choice, since any honour card in partner's hand will help to establish the suit.

♠ 9 3		
♡ A 6 2	*North*	*South*
◇ Q 7 6 3	1 ♠	1 NT
♣ Q 9 4 2	3 ♠	3 NT

The club lead is preferable to the diamond, because the presence of the nine gives a little extra security.

♠ J 9 6 5		
♡ A 9 7 2	*South*	*North*
◇ 10 5 3	2 NT	—
♣ K 2		

The lead from a four-card suit headed by an ace is not usually very productive. Here it is better to lead a spade and hope that the ace of hearts will serve as an entry when the spades are established. A further point is that if the spade attack proves fruitless you may still have a chance to make something of the hearts, but an initial heart lead that turns out badly is likely to leave you with no second chance.

Defence

♠ A 9 6 5 2
♡ K J 10 4
◇ 8
♣ J 4 3

South	North
1 NT	3 NT

With a five-card suit you need no longer be reluctant to lead away from an ace. Here a spade lead is much less dangerous than a heart, and the chances of establishing some spade tricks are quite bright.

♠ 10 4
♡ K Q 10 9 3
◇ J 10 9 3
♣ 7 2

South	North
2 ♣	2 ◇
2 NT	3 NT

In a team or rubber game you would start with the king of hearts, as this clearly gives the best chance of beating the contract. The lead will lose more often than it gains, however, and at pairs the knave of diamonds is the wiser choice.

The opponents will occasionally open with a gambling three no trumps, even in the pairs game. When they do you should try, if it is at all possible, to have a look at dummy before surrendering the lead.

♠ K Q J 7 3
♡ J 7 4
◇ A Q 6
♣ 6 4

South	North
3 NT	—

To start with the king of spades would be to put all your eggs in the one basket. The ace of diamonds gives you a three-way option. You can continue diamonds if partner encourages, or switch to either major suit depending on dummy's holding. The advantages of having a look at dummy will more than compensate for the odd occasion when the lead of the ace of diamonds presents declarer with a trick.

With an entryless hand it may still be worth while establishing your long suit if only to conceal your entryless state from the

The Lead

declarer. Sometimes the use of a little guile will enable you to run the suit anyway.

		South	North
♠ 8		*South*	*North*
♡ K Q J 10 4		1 NT	2 ♣
◇ 9 6 4 2		2 ♡	3 NT
♣ 10 7 5			

The lead of the queen of hearts might persuade South to win the first round in the hope that your partner failed to unblock with king and another. Whether partner would return the suit on gaining the lead is another matter.

		North	South
♠ A Q		*North*	*South*
♡ 8 7 3		1 ♠	2 ◇
◇ J 9 5 2		3 ♠	3 NT
♣ A 9 8 3			

On this bidding your partner cannot have much high-card strength, and the best hope for the defence lies in the club suit. A careful defender will lead the eight or nine rather than the three, for the full deal might be as shown below.

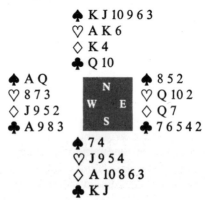

```
                    ♠ K J 10 9 6 3
                    ♡ A K 6
                    ◇ K 4
                    ♣ Q 10
     ♠ A Q                           ♠ 8 5 2
     ♡ 8 7 3          N              ♡ Q 10 2
     ◇ J 9 5 2     W     E           ◇ Q 7
     ♣ A 9 8 3          S            ♣ 7 6 5 4 2
                    ♠ 7 4
                    ♡ J 9 5 4
                    ◇ A 10 8 6 3
                    ♣ K J
```

Leads against suit contracts at pairs are again dominated to some extent by the need for safety. A lot depends on whether the opponents have found a fit, and the level at which they play.

Defence

When the opponents locate a fit at a low level, a trump is often the best lead. This applies particularly when you have a balanced hand with strength in the side suits.

♠ 9 7 6
♡ J 4
◇ A Q J 5
♣ K J 7 2

	South	North
	1 NT	2 ♣
	2 ♠	—

Dummy will be short in one of the minor suits, and you should therefore lead a trump to reduce ruffing values.

Against high-level contracts a blind trump lead is more hazardous, but it will usually be right when dummy has advertised ruffing values and you have a good holding in declarer's side suit.

♠ Q 4 2
♡ 7 5 4
◇ K Q 9 3
♣ Q 10 6

	South	North
	1 ♠	2 ♣
	2 ◇	3 ♠
	4 ♠	—

There is no need to be nervous about leading away from the queen of spades on this bidding. Any trump trick you sacrifice usually comes back with interest. The full hand:

♠ K 7 5
♡ Q 8 6 2
◇ 6
♣ A J 8 4 3

♠ Q 4 2   ♠ 10 6
♡ 7 5 4   ♡ A J 10
◇ K Q 9 3   ◇ 10 7 5 4
♣ Q 10 6   ♣ K 9 7 2

♠ A J 9 8 3
♡ K 9 3
◇ A J 8 2
♣ 5

The trump lead holds South to nine tricks, while any other attack allows him to make ten.

The Lead

When the opponents find a fit through the use of some distributional gadget such as the Roman Two Diamond opening, a trump lead is often best.

♠ 8 4		
♡ 10 6 3	*North*	*South*
◇ A K J 7 2	2 ◇	2 ♠
♣ 8 7 3	3 ♠	4 ♠

Resist the temptation to start with a top diamond here. Diamonds are almost certainly dummy's short suit, and if you have a trick to cash in the suit it will not run away. South is marked with a weak hand, and what strength your partner has in hearts and clubs is favourably placed. You should therefore lead a trump to reduce the declarer's chance of playing a successful cross-ruff.

A trump lead stands out in all cases where it is clear that the opponents are bidding on distribution rather than high-card strength.

♠ Q 10 7 5	*Game all. Dealer West*		
♡ 7 5	*West* *North*	*East*	*South*
◇ K 8 3	1 NT 2 ♣	3 ◇	3 ♡
♣ A K 8 4	— —	Double	All pass

North's two-club bid was Astro, showing hearts and a lower-ranking suit, and although your side must have the balance of strength the opponents have bought the hand. Clearly they must expect to make tricks by ruffing, and you should therefore attack with a trump lead. There is no need to play a top club in order to have a look at dummy, because you know what dummy contains—lots of clubs and hearts.

The trump lead earns a top score and anything else a bottom, for the full hand is:

Defence

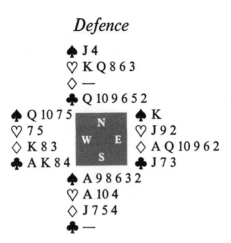

```
              ♠ J 4
              ♡ K Q 8 6 3
              ◇ —
              ♣ Q 10 9 6 5 2
♠ Q 10 7 5                    ♠ K
♡ 7 5            N            ♡ J 9 2
◇ K 8 3      W     E          ◇ A Q 10 9 6 2
♣ A K 8 4       S             ♣ J 7 3
              ♠ A 9 8 6 3 2
              ♡ A 10 4
              ◇ J 7 5 4
              ♣ —
```

There are not many defenders who would automatically make the proper lead in the following case.

Love all. Dealer South

	South	West	North	East
♠ K Q 10 8 7	South	West	North	East
♡ 9 3	4 ◇	—	—	4 ♡
◇ K	—	—	5 ◇	—
♣ K Q 9 4 2	—	Double	All pass	

It is tempting to hang on to the king of diamonds in the hope that the declarer will take a trump finesse into your hand. That is wishful thinking, however. If you ask yourself how the declarer might conceivably come to eleven tricks the answer will be plain —by ruffing. You should therefore lead the king of diamonds in order to cut down the number of possible ruffs in dummy.

Against high-level contracts a lead away from a king or queen is dangerous and therefore normally undesirable at pairs. There are occasions, however, when the bidding cries out for such a lead. When both declarer and dummy have bid side suits you will be able to recognize that any losers declarer may have in the fourth suit will certainly be discarded if you do not attack immediately.

The Lead

	South	North
♠ Q 6 3	1 ♠	2 ◇
♡ 8 4	2 ♡	3 ◇
◇ 10 7 6 2	3 ♡	4 ♡
♣ K 9 6 5		

This is not the occasion for a passive trump lead. Attack with the five of clubs before South's clubs can be ditched on dummy's diamonds.

The full hand:

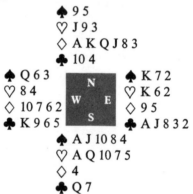

```
              ♠ 9 5
              ♡ J 9 3
              ◇ A K Q J 8 3
              ♣ 10 4
♠ Q 6 3                      ♠ K 7 2
♡ 8 4                        ♡ K 6 2
◇ 10 7 6 2                   ◇ 9 5
♣ K 9 6 5                    ♣ A J 8 3 2
              ♠ A J 10 8 4
              ♡ A Q 10 7 5
              ◇ 4
              ♣ Q 7
```

The contract is unbeatable, but the club lead is needed to hold the declarer to ten tricks.

When you have pushed the opponents to the five-level, it usually pays to follow up your aggressive bidding with an attacking lead.

North-South game. Dealer South

	South	West	North	East
♠ Q J 10 7 4	1 ♡	1 ♠	2 ♣	3 ♠
♡ 9 5 4	4 ♡	—	—	4 ♠
◇ Q 7 3	—	—	5 ♡	All
♣ K Q				pass

If you have a spade trick there is no hurry to cash it. The lead that stands out is the three of diamonds. You must make sure of getting what diamond tricks you can before dummy's clubs become established.

Defence

The full hand:

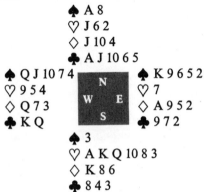

```
          ♠ A 8
          ♡ J 6 2
          ◇ J 10 4
          ♣ A J 10 6 5
♠ Q J 10 7 4              ♠ K 9 6 5 2
♡ 9 5 4          N         ♡ 7
◇ Q 7 3      W     E       ◇ A 9 5 2
♣ K Q          S          ♣ 9 7 2
          ♠ 3
          ♡ A K Q 10 8 3
          ◇ K 8 6
          ♣ 8 4 3
```

Against high-level contracts a singleton lead can be devastating, but it is important to be able to recognize the proper occasion for its use. The singleton lead is likely to be most effective when you have a weak hand, preferably with trump control.

♠ 10 8 5 2		
♡ A 7 5	*South*	*North*
◇ 8	1 ♡	2 ◇
♣ J 9 6 4 3	2 ♡	4 ♡

Here the singleton lead is ideal, for partner is sure to have at least one entry. You will be able to win the first round of trumps, put partner in, and get your ruff.

♠ A Q J	*Love all. Dealer South*			
♡ J 7 3	*South*	*West*	*North*	*East*
◇ 8	1 ♡	2 ♣	2 ◇	—
♣ K Q 10 7 6 3	2 ♡	—	4 ♡	All pass

Now the position is rather different. In a rubber or team game you might still try the singleton diamond lead as the best chance of defeating the contract. The lead will lose a trick more often than it gains one, however, and that rules it out for pairs. The proper lead is the orthodox king of clubs.

143

The Lead

A good time to look for an alternative to a singleton lead is when you have four trumps, or when you have reason to suppose your partner may have four.

	South	North
♠ 5	1 ♡	1 NT
♡ 9 8 7 5	3 ♣	3 ♡
◇ K 9 7 6 4	4 ♡	—
♣ A 9 3		

Here the forcing game offers the best chance and you should lead your fourth-highest diamond. The full hand:

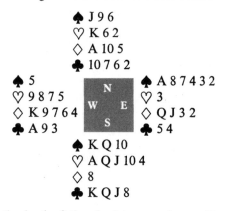

Note that the lead of the singleton spade would present the declarer with his contract, whereas the diamond attack gives him little chance.

Leading Against Slams

Any slam that is made against you is likely to give you a poor score. You should normally go all out to beat the slam, and consequently there is little difference between pairs and other forms of bridge when it comes to choosing a lead against a slam. On balance aggression will pay.

Nevertheless, even at the six-level it can be costly to allow the declarer to make an overtrick, and so at pairs there is a greater

Defence

incentive to cash an ace if you have one. In such cases the bidding is the only guide you have. If it appears that the declarer will have to look for his tricks, it will normally be best to hang on to your ace and make a neutral lead. If the bidding is aggressive and confident, on the other hand, it may be wise to cash out.

		North	*South*
♠ A Q 8 7			
♡ 2		*North*	*South*
◇ J 10 9 7		1 ♡	3 NT
♣ 8 7 6 4		4 NT	6 NT

The opponents appear to have balanced hands and there is little danger of losing your ace of spades. The natural lead of the knave of diamonds is therefore indicated. But if the bidding had gone as follows the position would be different.

		North	*South*
♠ A Q 8 7			
♡ 2		*North*	*South*
◇ J 10 9 7		1 ♡	3 ♣
♣ 8 7 6 4		4 ♡	6 NT

Now your ace of spades should hit the table at just under the speed of light, for you expect the full hand to be something like:

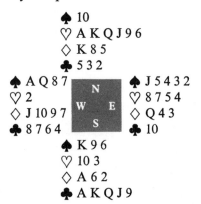

South has thirteen tricks unless you cash out at trick one.
Holding the two top honours in a suit, some players like to lead

145

The Lead

the ace and others the king. Whichever method you favour, you should lead the king against a slam if you are lucky enough to have an ace-king holding. The lead of a king against a slam demands a distributional echo from your partner, and this should enable you to determine whether or not you can take a second trick in the suit. Players do occasionally bid slams when they have two quick losers in a suit.

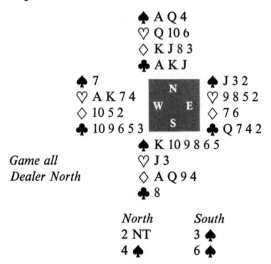

```
                    ♠ A Q 4
                    ♡ Q 10 6
                    ◇ K J 8 3
                    ♣ A K J
        ♠ 7                        ♠ J 3 2
        ♡ A K 7 4                  ♡ 9 8 5 2
        ◇ 10 5 2                   ◇ 7 6
        ♣ 10 9 6 5 3              ♣ Q 7 4 2
                    ♠ K 10 9 8 6 5
Game all            ♡ J 3
Dealer North        ◇ A Q 9 4
                    ♣ 8
```

North	South
2 NT	3 ♠
4 ♠	6 ♠

On your lead of the king of hearts the declarer will drop the knave, but your partner's nine tells you that the ace will stand up.

One of the least-publicized aspects of defensive play is the art of subtle misdirection when you have potential trump winners.

		Game all. Dealer South	
♠ Q 5		South	North
♡ 9 8		1 ♣	2 ♠
◇ Q J 6 2		3 ◇	4 ◇
♣ 10 7 6 3 2		4 ♡	6 ◇

Many players would lead the nine of hearts without too much thought, but this lead is psychologically inept. It will surely

146

Defence

register with the declarer that you appear to be short in hearts, and therefore quite likely long in trumps, and he will play the trumps correctly if he has an honour in each hand.

The three of clubs is the proper choice of lead. By letting the declarer know about your club length you hope to persuade him that you are short in trumps. He will then be more likely to mis-play the hand and allow you to make two trump tricks.

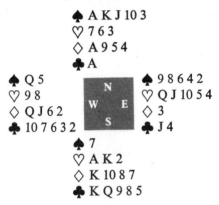

```
            ♠ A K J 10 3
            ♡ 7 6 3
            ◇ A 9 5 4
            ♣ A
  ♠ Q 5                      ♠ 9 8 6 4 2
  ♡ 9 8            N         ♡ Q J 10 5 4
  ◇ Q J 6 2     W     E      ◇ 3
  ♣ 10 7 6 3 2     S         ♣ J 4
            ♠ 7
            ♡ A K 2
            ◇ K 10 8 7
            ♣ K Q 9 8 5
```

There is, of course, no certainty of success, but after a club lead the declarer might well lead the ace of diamonds at trick two and continue with another diamond, thereby ruining his slam.

On the nine of hearts lead the declarer would have a much better chance of getting it right. After winning the first trick he would probably lead a club to the ace, a diamond to his king, and run the second round of diamonds.

The reverse situation arises when you have a singleton trump and wish to protect your partner's potential trump winners. To give the impression of length in trumps you should make a short suit lead, or at least choose a card that might be interpreted as a short suit lead.

When partner doubles a high cue bid to indicate a lead you naturally sit up and take notice, but does it register with equal force when partner fails to make such a double?

147

The Lead

	South	North
♠ 8 5 4	1 ◇	1 ♠
♡ J 10 9	3 NT	4 ◇
◇ 6 4	5 ♣	5 ♡
♣ 9 7 4 3 2	6 ◇	—

Nothing could look more natural than the lead of the knave of hearts, but partner had an opportunity to double five hearts and failed to do so. You should therefore lead a club. The full hand might be:

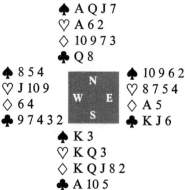

<pre>
                    ♠ A Q J 7
                    ♡ A 6 2
                    ◇ 10 9 7 3
                    ♣ Q 8
     ♠ 8 5 4   ♠ 10 9 6 2
     ♡ J 10 9   N   ♡ 8 7 5 4
     ◇ 6 4   W   E   ◇ A 5
     ♣ 9 7 4 3 2   S   ♣ K J 6
                    ♠ K 3
                    ♡ K Q 3
                    ◇ K Q J 8 2
                    ♣ A 10 5
</pre>

It is not often that you will have a problem when partner makes a Lightner double.

	South	West	North	East
♠ 8 6 2	2 ♠	—	3 ♣	3 ◇
♡ 9 6	3 ♠	—	4 ◇	—
◇ 9 3	6 ♠	—	—	Double
♣ K J 10 6 4 3	All pass			

Clearly partner is void in clubs, the suit first bid by dummy. Which club should you lead? The knave would be the normal card, but the ace is likely to be in dummy and that is a good reason for leading the king. It might be vital to remove an entry card from dummy at trick one, for the full deal could be:

Defence

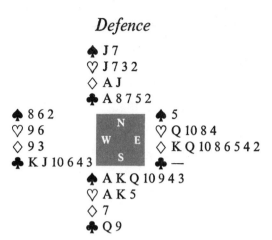

♠ J 7
♡ J 7 3 2
◇ A J
♣ A 8 7 5 2

♠ 8 6 2
♡ 9 6
◇ 9 3
♣ K J 10 6 4 3

♠ 5
♡ Q 10 8 4
◇ K Q 10 8 6 5 4 2
♣ —

♠ A K Q 10 9 4 3
♡ A K 5
◇ 7
♣ Q 9

If you lead the knave and South makes the right guess, he will eventually make his slam by squeezing East in hearts and diamonds. But the lead of the king allows East to ruff away the ace and destroy the squeeze by switching to diamonds.

Even if no squeeze is possible a crafty declarer might induce your partner to ruff a loser if you lead the knave of clubs. The full hand might equally well be as follows:

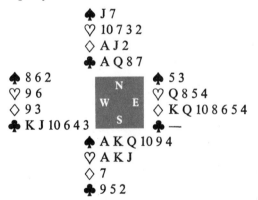

♠ J 7
♡ 10 7 3 2
◇ A J 2
♣ A Q 8 7

♠ 8 6 2
♡ 9 6
◇ 9 3
♣ K J 10 6 4 3

♠ 5 3
♡ Q 8 5 4
◇ K Q 10 8 6 5 4
♣ —

♠ A K Q 10 9 4
♡ A K J
◇ 7
♣ 9 5 2

If declarer played low from dummy on your lead of the knave of clubs, could you blame partner for ruffing and hoping you could score a trump or a heart trick?

The effect of the initial lead on subsequent defence is a subject

149

The Lead

that is hard to pin down. In general, the defenders should try to consolidate their position when they have got off to a good start, taking no risks that might surrender their advantage.

```
                        ♠ K 10
Game all                ♡ 9 5
Dealer South            ◇ 8 7 2
                        ♣ A Q 10 9 64
    South   North              ♠ 7 6 5
    1 ♡     2 ♣                 ♡ K Q 6 3
    2 NT    3 NT                ◇ Q J 5
                               ♣ K 8 3
```

West leads the three of diamonds to your knave and South plays the six. You continue with the queen of diamonds, South playing the ten and West the five. What next?

Since your partner cannot have an entry, there is no point in leading another diamond. To defeat the contract the best shot is to lead a small heart in the hope that partner has the ten and will be allowed to make it. A heart return would then establish another trick in the suit before your king of clubs is knocked out.

But you should not be thinking about beating the contract here. Holding declarer to nine tricks will be enough to give you a good score. Presumably partner might have led a spade initially, and this would have given South at least ten tricks. Be grateful that your partner hit the jackpot by leading a diamond instead, and make sure of your fourth defensive trick by leading the king of hearts.

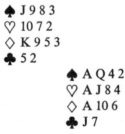

```
        ♠ J 9 8 3
        ♡ 10 7 2
        ◇ K 9 5 3
        ♣ 5 2
                    ♠ A Q 4 2
                    ♡ A J 8 4
                    ◇ A 10 6
                    ♣ J 7
```

Defence

When your opening lead turns out poorly you should be prepared to take risks in order to make up for the lost ground.

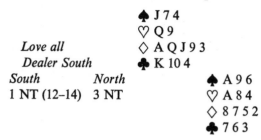

Love all
Dealer South

South	North
1 NT (12–14)	3 NT

♠ J 7 4
♡ Q 9
◇ A Q J 9 3
♣ K 10 4

♠ A 9 6
♡ A 8 4
◇ 8 7 5 2
♣ 7 6 3

West leads the queen of clubs against the three no trump contract, and the declarer wins with the ace. On the lead of the five of spades your partner plays the two, and you take dummy's knave with your ace. How should you continue?

Partner is marked with one of the red kings, probably the king of hearts since South did not attack diamonds immediately. The opening lead appears to have given declarer an extra trick in clubs. This might not matter if it was an automatic lead from a five-card suit, but if partner has four hearts headed by the king and knave it is possible that an original heart lead would have defeated the contract.

You should therefore try for four heart tricks in an attempt to draw level with any who lead hearts originally. The way to do that is to lead the eight of hearts on the first round. This risks allowing the declarer to make twelve tricks if he has the king of hearts after all, but it is a risk that ought to be taken.

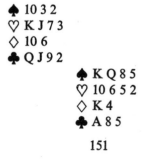

♠ 10 3 2
♡ K J 7 3
◇ 10 6
♣ Q J 9 2

♠ K Q 8 5
♡ 10 6 5 2
◇ K 4
♣ A 8 5

PART FOUR

Sacrifice

10

Bidding

ONE of the surest ways of falling below par is to allow the opponents to make a game contract when you might have registered a smaller minus score by sacrificing. An equally good way of getting a bottom score, of course, is by making a phantom sacrifice against a game bid which cannot be made. Good judgement is needed in order to steer a safe course between Scylla of faint-heartedness and the Charybdis of the phantom, but there are certain basic principles which serve as navigational aids.

Competitive bidding tactics remain essentially the same at the game level, but the mathematics of the situation are altered by the prospect of the game bonus.

Let us first consider the position where the enemy has the balance of strength and you are contemplating a sacrifice. As always in the contested auction, the vulnerability will be a major factor. At favourable vulnerability you can afford to be quite frisky, for three down doubled will give you a good score if the enemy game is on. At equal vulnerability you have to draw in your horns a little. Two down doubled is the most you can afford, but that still gives plenty of scope for profitable sacrificing. At adverse vulnerability you cannot afford to go more than one down if the opponents double, and that leaves too slender a margin for error. You can seldom be sure of going no more than one down, and you should therefore expect to have a chance of making your contract when you outbid the enemy at adverse vulnerability.

The groundwork for successful sacrifice bidding is normally laid at an early stage in the auction. What happens at the one-

Sacrifice

level will very often determine the course of events at the five-level. That is one of the reasons why, when vulnerability conditions permit, it pays to open light, overcall on minimal values, and double for takeout with alacrity and not much else.

♠ K J 7 6 4 2
♡ Q 10 5   *Game all. Dealer West*
◇ 6 3   *West*   *North*   *East*   *South*
♣ K 9   1 ◇   —   1 ♡   ?

With both opponents bidding and partner silent, it is dangerous to put in an overcall of one spade. You might be doubled and set 1,100, or even 1,400. But that is looking on the darkest side, and there are three good reasons for overcalling. You will indicate a good lead against a no trump or suit contract, you might find a fit and be able to contest the part-score, or you could pave the way for a profitable sacrifice. It is the last reason we are concerned with here. The full hand could be as follows:

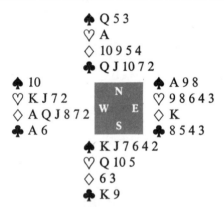

                    ♠ Q 5 3
                    ♡ A
                    ◇ 10 9 5 4
                    ♣ Q J 10 7 2
♠ 10   ♠ A 9 8
♡ K J 7 2   ♡ 9 8 6 4 3
◇ A Q J 8 7 2   ◇ K
♣ A 6   ♣ 8 5 4 3
                    ♠ K J 7 6 4 2
                    ♡ Q 10 5
                    ◇ 6 3
                    ♣ K 9

If you put in an overcall of one spade the bidding is likely to proceed:

West	*North*	*East*	*South*
1 ◇	—	1 ♡	1 ♠
4 ♡	4 ♠	Double	All pass

Four spades doubled costs only 200 points, and if the opponents press on to five hearts you may actually achieve a plus score.

This is the most attractive fringe benefit of sacrifice bidding. The opponents do sometimes bid on and get too high. Then you will beat par handsomely by registering a plus score when you were booked for a minus.

When the enemy bid on to the five-level it will generally be a mistake to compete further. In such cases your push has done its job, and you should be content to allow the opponents to play the hand. On no account should you double. If the enemy contract is going down there is not the slightest need to double; you will get a fine score anyway. And if by chance the opponents can make their five-level contract, a double would convert a near-average board into a bottom for you.

Raising Partner's Overcall

At favourable vulnerability when your partner makes a simple overcall and you have a weakish hand, you will expect to get a minus score. The balance of power clearly lies with the opponents, who are probably on the way to a game contract. If you have some support for partner's suit a good sacrifice may be available, however. Sometimes a glance at your hand will be enough to tell you that it must be right to sacrifice. At other times you will not be sure whether a sacrifice is advisable or not. Then you must refer the decision to your partner by giving him an accurate picture of your hand. There are many such hands in which both partners have to play an intelligent part in deciding whether or not to sacrifice. Without defensive co-operation the decision is often no more than a guess.

Let us first look at what not to do.

Sacrifice

	♠ 9 6	
	♡ Q J 10 4	
	◇ 7 2	
	♣ A K 10 8 3	

♠ A J 7 5 4 3		♠ K 8 2
♡ K 9 2		♡ 6 5
◇ 9 6 5 3		◇ K 10 4
♣ —		♣ J 9 6 4 2

Love all
Dealer South

♠ Q 10
♡ A 8 7 3
◇ A Q J 8
♣ Q 7 5

South	West	North	East
1 ♡	1 ♠	3 ♡	—
4 ♡	—	—	4 ♠
Double	All pass		

On careful defence four spades went two down at a cost of
300 points. This was a poor result for East and West, since most
pairs picked up 50 by defending against four hearts, the defence
taking two spades, a club ruff and the king of hearts. East was the
culprit, of course. He considered his hand not good enough to
give a raise at the three-level and subsequently took a unilateral
decision to sacrifice over four hearts.

That is trap bidding of the worst kind. With a hand containing
support for partner's suit and a modicum of defensive potential
the proper procedure is to give a minimum raise at the first opportunity, stretching to do so if necessary. If East raises to three
spades over North's three heart bid he can then relax and leave
all further decisions to his partner. If West chooses to sacrifice,
well and good. But if West decides to defend against four hearts,
as he would do in this case, East will be happy to co-operate.

Basically there are just three courses of action open to a defender who has a weak hand with support for partner's overcall.
He can pass, give a minimum raise, or raise to the limit. His choice
of action should depend on what sort of a weak hand he has.

Bidding

Suppose that the auction goes as follows:

South	West	North	East
1 ♡	1 ♠	2 ♡	?

(a) ♠ Q J 3   (b) ♠ A J 10 5   (c) ♠ J 8 7 4
   ♡ 7 2   ♡ 6   ♡ K J 10 3
   ◇ J 9 6 4   ◇ 10 9 2   ◇ Q J 6
   ♣ A 10 7 2   ♣ 10 8 5 3 2 ♣ 5 2

On hand (a) East has trump support for his partner along with some defensive values. He cannot be sure whether an enemy game can be made or not. The proper action, therefore, is to give a minimum raise and leave the rest to partner. If West pushes on over four hearts it should be a good save, while if he passes there should be a chance of defeating the enemy game.

Hand (b) is a straightforward case. East's hand is so defenceless that he can be sure four hearts will make. Four spades is likely to be a good sacrifice and, rather than bid up slowly, East should say four spades immediately. An advance sacrifice of this type always offers the best chance of pushing the opponents overboard. Reluctant to accept the non-vulnerable penalty, they may press on to an unmakable contract at the five-level.

With hand (c) East should pass. Although he has four-card trump support his values are mainly defensive in nature. He would expect to defeat an enemy contract of four hearts and should therefore do nothing which might encourage his partner to sacrifice in four spades.

When Not to Sacrifice

The last example raises an important point. Light opening bids and overcalls are made partly in order to take out an option on an eventual sacrifice, but you must not always choose to exercise this option. One factor that should influence you against sacrificing is the presence of defensive values in your hand.

Sacrifice

	East-West game. Dealer East			
♠ A 10 9 6 3	West	North	East	South
♡ J 10 9 5			1 ♣	1 ♠
◇ K 10	2 ♡	2 ♠	3 ♡	—
♣ 7 3	4 ♡	—	—	?

Partner has at most a singleton heart, and so four spades will not be expensive. But even minus 100 will be too expensive if four hearts cannot be made, and there is a good chance that you and your partner can take four tricks in defence. You should therefore pass and hope for the best.

An obvious occasion for declining to sacrifice is when you have pushed the opponents into game.

	East-West game. Dealer West			
♠ Q 8 7 3	West	North	East	South
♡ 7	1 ♡	1 ♠	2 ◇	2 ♠
◇ K 9 4	—	—	3 ♡	—
♣ J 9 7 6 4	—	3 ♠	—	—
	4 ♡	—	—	?

You don't have much in the way of defence, and four spades could be a cheap sacrifice. Nevertheless, you should choose to defend. Partner could, after all, have left the opponents to play in a part-score contract. You should assume that he knows what he is doing and was right to push once more. Very likely he has a couple of trump tricks as a surprise for the declarer. At any rate, it seems clear from the bidding that not many East-West pairs will reach a game contract. A sacrifice will therefore be too costly even if you get out for 300.

This point is often overlooked. A successful sacrifice bid will bring you in a good score only if most of the field reach game on your opponents' cards. When your opponents stagger into game after an unconvincing bidding sequence, therefore, it is usually wise to forget about sacrificing and defend instead.

At favourable vulnerability it pays to be bold with your sacrifice bids.

Bidding

♠ A
♡ A Q 10
♦ 9 6
♣ Q J 10 8 7 4 2

North-South game. Dealer South

South	West	North	East
1 ♣	—	4 ♠	?

You cannot be certain that four spades will make, but it seems highly probable. You require very little from partner, however, to make five clubs a profitable sacrifice. At pairs this sort of risk should be taken.

When the problem occurred the full hand was:

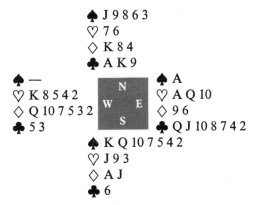

```
              ♠ J 9 8 6 3
              ♡ 7 6
              ♦ K 8 4
              ♣ A K 9
♠ —                        ♠ A
♡ K 8 5 4 2       N        ♡ A Q 10
♦ Q 10 7 5 3 2  W   E      ♦ 9 6
♣ 5 3             S        ♣ Q J 10 8 7 4 2
              ♠ K Q 10 7 5 4 2
              ♡ J 9 3
              ♦ A J
              ♣ 6
```

North would have been happy enough to double five clubs but he didn't get the chance, for South went on to five spades. Plus 100 was a magnificent score for East-West, but even minus 500 (on double-dummy defence to five clubs doubled) would have been above average.

Nobody likes to place too much reliance upon the enemy bidding, but there are times when it is right to trust the opponents. A trashy collection of cards can take on a new look when the opponents seem reluctant to accept a penalty.

♠ 9 6 5 3
♡ 10 9 7 6 5 2
♦ 9 4
♣ 5

Love all. Dealer South

South	West	North	East
1 NT	Double	3 NT	?
(12–14)			

Sacrifice

Most players would not dream of bidding on the East hand above. But think for a moment about the opponents' sequence. What sort of bidding is that? Why did North not redouble if he has a strong all-round hand?

There can be only one answer. North has a minor suit hand. He is short in the majors and, knowing there would be no worthwhile penalty if he redoubled, he jumped to three no trumps to stop you and your partner getting together.

It is possible that partner has the beating of three no trumps in his own hand, but this must be very much against the odds. Three no trumps will probably be made, but there *must* be a good save for you in one of the major suits and you should therefore bid four hearts. Do not be afraid to go against the field when your judgement tells you the action is right. Other players may not be faced with the problem anyway, for the auction could follow a quite different course at some tables. The full hand:

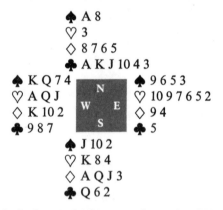

```
              ♠ A 8
              ♡ 3
              ♢ 8 7 6 5
              ♣ A K J 10 4 3
♠ K Q 7 4                    ♠ 9 6 5 3
♡ A Q J          N          ♡ 10 9 7 6 5 2
♢ K 10 2     W     E         ♢ 9 4
♣ 9 8 7          S          ♣ 5
              ♠ J 10 2
              ♡ K 8 4
              ♢ A Q J 3
              ♣ Q 6 2
```

Four hearts is, in fact, unlucky to go down, but North is likely to bid on to an unmakable five clubs.

Who is Sacrificing?

When the high-card points of the pack are evenly divided between the two sides, it can be hard to tell who is sacrificing. If

Bidding

the opponents compete with confidence at the game level it is safe to assume that the distribution will be wild. Honours in your long suits should to some extent be discounted for defensive purposes. The trickiest decisions a pairs player is called upon to make occur in situations like this.

Love all. Dealer East

	West	North	East	South
♠ 5			1 ◇	2 ♣
♡ A 9 6 4				
◇ 10 7 6	—	2 ♡	2 ♠	4 ♡
♣ A K 10 9 5	4 ♠	—	—	?

You cannot be sure if four spades will make, but it seems unlikely that your partner will be able to make eleven tricks in hearts. In a team game there would be no real problem. The proper course would be to bid five hearts, for you could afford to concede a small swing, but not a large one, on a wrong guess.

At pairs the problem is not so simple, for the size of the swing does not enter into the matter. You must make up your mind whether four spades is going to make or not and back your judgement. The fact that your partner passed four spades should mean that he is not entirely devoid of defensive tricks, but your lack of values in diamonds should probably influence you to bid five hearts. The full hand:

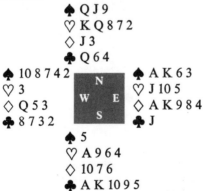

```
              ♠ Q J 9
              ♡ K Q 8 7 2
              ◇ J 3
              ♣ Q 6 4
♠ 10 8 7 4 2         N         ♠ A K 6 3
♡ 3              W       E      ♡ J 10 5
◇ Q 5 3             S          ◇ A K 9 8 4
♣ 8 7 3 2                      ♣ J
              ♠ 5
              ♡ A 9 6 4
              ◇ 10 7 6
              ♣ A K 10 9 5
```

In the last hand if South decided that four spades was likely to

163

Sacrifice

go down he should, of course, pass rather than double. As always when the strength is evenly divided, there is no need to double. Just making the right decision will give you a good score. And if your decision to defend is wrong, as it is bound to be sometimes, your pass may still salvage a few match-points when others double.

Here is another typical case.

♠ A K Q 9 7 6 4   *Game all. Dealer South*
♡ A 7 3

South	West	North	East
2 ♠	Double	4 ♠	4 NT
—	5 ♣	—	—
?			

♢ 10 2
♣ 6

It is almost impossible to tell whether you could have made four spades or whether the opponents can make five clubs. You are certainly not likely to make five spades, and the best chance is to pass and hope the enemy have made a phantom sacrifice. The full hand might be:

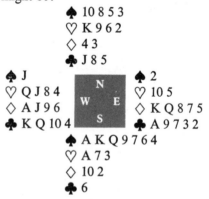

```
              ♠ 10 8 5 3
              ♡ K 9 6 2
              ♢ 4 3
              ♣ J 8 5
♠ J                        ♠ 2
♡ Q J 8 4      N           ♡ 10 5
♢ A J 9 6   W     E        ♢ K Q 8 7 5
♣ K Q 10 4     S           ♣ A 9 7 3 2
              ♠ A K Q 9 7 6 4
              ♡ A 7 3
              ♢ 10 2
              ♣ 6
```

When to Double

When your side holds the balance of power and it is clear that the opponents are sacrificing, your choice lies between bidding on and doubling. Such decisions are again often balanced on a razor's edge and there is no substitute for fine judgement.

Bidding

♠ K Q J 8		*Love all. Dealer East*		
♡ K J 8 3	*West*	*North*	*East*	*South*
◇ 5			1 ◇	Double
♣ K Q 9 4	3 ◇	4 ♡	5 ◇	?

This hand clearly belongs to your side. You would have felt fairly confident of making game in hearts, but your lack of aces makes eleven tricks doubtful. This is not a decision which you should leave to your partner. Tell him about your doubts by doubling. This does not prohibit him from bidding on if he has a suitable hand.

The penalty in five diamonds doubled may not compensate you for the loss of the game, but the bidding is likely to go the same way at the other tables and plus 300—or perhaps plus 100—may be the maximum available for North-South.

The full hand:

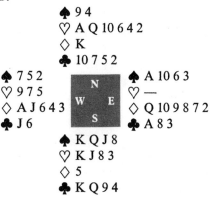

```
            ♠ 9 4
            ♡ A Q 10 6 4 2
            ◇ K
            ♣ 10 7 5 2
♠ 7 5 2              ♠ A 10 6 3
♡ 9 7 5      N       ♡ —
◇ A J 6 4 3  W   E   ◇ Q 10 9 8 7 2
♣ J 6          S     ♣ A 8 3
            ♠ K Q J 8
            ♡ K J 8 3
            ◇ 5
            ♣ K Q 9 4
```

In the above hand the decision to double rather than allow yourself to be pushed too high was fairly straightforward, but this is not always the case. Often you will feel reluctant to accept an inadequate penalty. When you judge that most of the other pairs will be playing in game on your cards it is right to press on to the five-level.

Sacrifice

♠ A K 10 7 3	*North-South game. Dealer West*		
♡ A 9 4	*West*	*North*	*East*	*South*
◇ K 9 6 5	—	—	1 ♣	Double
♣ 2	2 NT	Double	3 ♣	3 ♠
	—	4 ♠	—	—
	5 ♣	—	—	?

Partner was unable to open the bidding and there is no guarantee that you can make more than ten tricks in spades. However, East appears to have made an unusual psychic opening bid which enabled his partner to find the sacrifice at the five-level. At other tables it is likely that North and South will reach four spades without interference. In that case the one thing you must not do is accept a penalty of 300 or 500 which could give you a bottom score. You are to some extent fixed by the opponents' bidding, and in spite of the risk you should try for 650 by bidding five spades. With any luck the full hand may turn out to be:

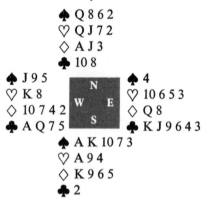

A double of five clubs would yield only 300 points, while five spades can be made by careful play.

Sacrificing Against Slams

In theory you can afford to lose 900 points sacrificing against a non-vulnerable slam, and 1,400 against a vulnerable one. But in

Bidding

practice such large minuses will rarely be worth many match-points. More often than not half the field will fail to bid the slam, and your sacrifice would then give you an average score at best.

If there appears to be any chance at all of beating the slam it is better to defend. There are many imponderables to consider, and it is not often that you will be able to predict with any certainty that the opponents will make their slam.

The only time when it is undeniably right to sacrifice is when (*a*) you are fairly sure the slam will make, and (b) you are confident of keeping the penalty to less than the value of an enemy *game*.

	East-West game. Dealer East			
	West	North	East	South
♠ K Q 9 5 2			1 ♣	1 ♠
♡ 9	2 ♠	4 ♠	—	—
◇ Q 10 8 5 4 3	5 ♣	—	5 ◇	—
♣ 3	5 ♡	—	5 NT	—
	6 ♣	—	—	?

This is very confident bidding by the opponents. East made two grand slam tries before settling for six clubs. The small slam is likely to be on ice, and a sacrifice bid of six spades should pay in this case. You may easily keep the penalty to 500, thus beating those pairs who lose 620 as well as those who fail to sacrifice against the slam.

11

Dummy Play

SETTING your trick target in the play of sacrifice contracts is just a matter of simple arithmetic. Having worked out what the opposing game is worth, you concentrate on keeping your loss to a lower figure.

The bidding will inevitably take a different course at some tables and you may be sure that not all the pairs playing your way will sacrifice. Some will choose to defend, perhaps because their bidding methods are not so aggressive as yours, perhaps because they hate going down, perhaps for some other reason. You must try to ensure that you get a better score than those who defend against the enemy game.

Never admit the possibility of your having made a phantom sacrifice, for if that were the case you would be booked for a very poor match-point score. The assumption must always be that the enemy could have made their game and that your sacrifice will be worth while. It is only by assuming you have reached the par contract that you can maintain the essential consistency in bidding and play that is the mark of the winner.

In choosing between different lines of play, therefore, select the one that is compatible with the assumption that the enemy game would have made, even if this line is against the odds. The same considerations must be borne in mind when placing key cards in the opponents' hands. To play a hand beautifully for one off will bring your little credit and few match-points if your line of play works only when the enemy game fails.

Dummy Play

♠ Q 10 5
♡ A 7
◇ 9 8 6 5
♣ Q J 8 3

♠ J 2
♡ K 4
◇ 7 2
♣ A 10 9 7 6 5 2

Love all. Dealer North

West	North	East	South
—	—		3 ♣
Double	5 ♣	Double	All pass

West starts off with the ace of spades against your doubled contract of five clubs. He then switches to diamonds, leading the king, queen and knave. You ruff the third round, cross to the ace of hearts, and lead the queen of clubs on which East plays the four. Should you finesse or not?

This simple question is typical of the decisions you have to make when playing a sacrifice contract. Since you have two diamond and two spade losers you are certainly going to concede 300 in this contract. To lose a club as well would make it 500, which is more than an enemy game is worth. To earn any matchpoints at all, therefore, you must make the correct decision here.

The way to tackle such problems is to work out what you have in defence against an enemy game. Partner had rather more defence than you expected and it is clear that you would win three tricks in the major suits against a contract of four hearts or four spades. For your sacrifice to be worth while, then, you must assume that you would not be able to make a club trick in defence.

In other words, West will need to be void in clubs to give you a good score and you should therefore finesse.

Sacrifice

♠ 7 4
♡ K 9 6 3
◇ A J 8 6 2
♣ 9 2

East-West game. Dealer East

West	North	East	South
		1 ♠	2 ♡
3 ♠	4 ♡	Double	All pass

♠ J 3
♡ A J 10 5 4
◇ K Q 3
♣ 10 7 4

West cashes the king and queen of spades and then leads a club to his partner's ace. West wins the club return with the knave and switches to the nine of diamonds. How do you play the trumps?

At most you have five losers and you are assured of a good score if the enemy can make four spades. That being so, you should assume there is no game on for the opponents and see what follows from that.

When only nine tricks can be made in spades East and West will score 140 at some tables and you must therefore hold your loss to 100. That means you cannot afford to lose a trump trick.

In defence you and your partner would have a maximum of four tricks—two diamonds and two hearts. But you would make these four tricks in defence only if the hearts break 2–2, and you should therefore play for the drop in trumps.

If the trumps prove to be a 3–1 after all, it will be no tragedy that you have to lose a trump trick. Your score of minus 300 will be an excellent one when other pairs are losing 620. It is when the trumps are 2–2 and no enemy game is on that you must at all costs avoid losing more than 100.

Dummy Play

♠ K 7
♡ K 4
♢ 10 7 6 3
♣ J 9 6 4 3

Love all. Dealer West

West	North	East	South
1 ♡	—	2 ♡	2 ♠

♠ A Q 10 8 6 3
♡ 6 3
♢ A 5 2
♣ 8 5

West	North	East	South
4 ♡	4 ♠	—	—
Double	All pass		

West leads the king of diamonds against your doubled contract of four spades and you win with the ace. How do you plan the play?

The situation looks grim. Partner's raise to four spades was eccentric, to say the least, and it is a safe bet that most of the other North-South pairs will choose to defend against four hearts.

In order to restrict the penalty to 300 in four spades doubled you will need to make six trump tricks and the king of hearts in addition to the diamond trick already in the bag. But if the heart ace is right for you it is wrong for the opponents—that is to say, the heart king would have scored in defence. It follows that with a normal spade break you would have four defensive tricks against a heart contract, and the pairs defending against four hearts will register plus scores.

That is a possibility which must not be entertained. You must assume that your idiot-partner did the right thing in bidding four spades and the only distribution to make that possible is a 4–1 trump break with the singleton in the West hand. Accordingly you should lead a spade to the king and, if the knave does not appear, finesse the ten on the way back.

Sacrifice

♠ K
♡ J 10 9 4
◇ J 8 7 4   *East-West game. Dealer South*
♣ A 6 4 3

	South	West	North	East
	1 ◇	—	1 ♡	1 ♠
♠ Q 3	2 ♡	2 ♠	3 ◇	4 ♠
♡ K Q 7 3	—	—	5 ◇	Double
◇ A Q 10 5 2	All pass			
♣ 8 7				

West leads the two of hearts against your doubled contract of
five diamonds. East wins the ace and returns the suit, and his
partner ruffs with the three of diamonds. On regaining the lead
with the ace of spades, East returns another heart and West ruffs
with the six of diamonds, West then leads the queen of clubs
which you win with dummy's ace. When you lead a trump from
the table East follows with the nine. Which card do you play from
hand?

You have lost two aces and two ruffs and there is still a club
to lose. That adds up to minus 500 and you therefore cannot
afford to misguess the trump position.

It is by no means certain that your partner's decision to sacrifice
in five diamonds was correct, but you must assume it to be correct
if you are to get any match-points on the board. Your play must
be based on the assumption that you would make no more than
three tricks in defence against four spades. A spade and a club
trick are certain, and so the one distribution you must not play
for is king and another diamond with East.

The finesse is therefore out of the question. You should play
the ace of diamonds in the hope that the king will now drop. On
that lie of the cards four spades would be a make, and your score
of minus 500 should be quite good.

Dummy Play

♠ 10 5 3 2
♡ 10 9 3
♢ 6 2
♣ K 9 4 3

♠ A 9 8 7 6 4
♡ A K 6
♢ 9 5
♣ 8 5

Game all. Dealer South

South	West	North	East
1 ♠	Double	2 ♠	Double
3 ♠	3 NT	—	—
4 ♠	Double	All pass	

Against your doubled contract of four spades West starts with the ace and king of diamonds. He then switches to the king of spades and East follows with the knave. How do you plan the play?

This looks like a hazardous enterprise. Since you are vulnerable you must not go more than two down. Will that be possible? Yes, if the ace of clubs is right, for then you will lose just two diamonds and one trick in each other suit.

But think of the implications if the king of clubs is behind the ace. That would mean that three no trumps is unmakable, for even if the enemy have six running tricks in diamonds they will be unable to come to nine tricks without giving up the lead in clubs. You have to assume that three no trumps is a make, therefore the ace of clubs will need to be in the East hand.

If East has the ace with not more than two other clubs there is a chance of holding the penalty to 500 by establishing the king of clubs for a heart discard. There is nothing else to play for and you should first give West his trump trick, taking care to preserve the four of spades in your hand. If West leads a club you will duck twice in dummy. If West leads a heart instead you will play the nine to force out East's honour card. Then by ducking twice in clubs you may be able to keep East off lead, while two trump entries remain on the table to establish and cash the king of clubs.

Sacrifice

```
♠ 7 6 4 2
♡ K Q 8 3
♢ 8 5                North-South game. Dealer North
♣ J 7 2              West    North    East    South
                      —       1 ♣     4 ♡
♠ A K 10 3            —       —       4 NT    —
♡ A J 10 9 6 5 2     5 ♢     5 ♡      Double  All pass
♢ —
♣ 10 4
```

West leads the nine of clubs against your doubled contract of five hearts. East wins the queen and continues with the king of clubs, his partner following with the three. East then leads the knave of spades which you win with the ace. Both opponents follow when you lead a trump to dummy's king. How should you continue?

It was an odd sort of auction with nobody quite knowing who was sacrificing. It is still possible for you to make your contract if East started with queen and knave doubleton in spades, but perhaps it is more likely that East has a 1–1–5–6 distribution. In that case five diamonds will be a make and you can be sure of a reasonable score if you limit the penalty to 200.

The safe way of guarding against a 4–1 spade break without prejudicing your chance of making the contract is to eliminate the diamonds first. Ruff a diamond high, play a trump to dummy and ruff the second diamond high.

Then cash the king of spades and discover your fate. If East shows out you can enter dummy once more in trumps to lead the knave of clubs and discard a spade from your hand. The enforced minor suit return from East will enable you to discard your last spade loser while ruffing in dummy.

Dummy Play

♠ 10 4 2
♡ J 3
♢ K 10 4
♣ A 10 9 5 4

East-West game. Dealer East

West	North	East	South
		1 ♠	2 ♢

♠ 5
♡ K 7 6 4
♢ A Q J 9 6 2
♣ 6 3

West	North	East	South
3 ♠	4 ♢	4 ♠	5 ♢
Double	All pass		

West cashes the queen of spades and then leads a trump to which East follows. How do you plan the play?

Some pairs will probably choose to defend against four spades on this hand. In defence you have a sure club and a likely heart trick, so if the sacrifice is not to prove a phantom the diamonds will need to break 3–1.

You have six trump tricks and the ace of clubs, and since you can afford to go no more than three down you will need to make at least one heart trick or a heart ruff. Is there any danger that you might not be able to do that? Yes, if West has both ace and queen of hearts along with the two outstanding trumps. It would therefore be dangerous to win the trump lead in dummy and lead a heart to your king. West might win and lead another trump, and later take out dummy's last trump when he gets in with the queen of hearts.

The safe play is to win the first trump in hand and lead a small heart towards the knave. If West goes up with the queen in order to lead a trump you must then make a heart trick. If the ace and queen of hearts are in different hands you will always be able to ruff a heart, of course. And if East has them both you don't care if he has the outstanding trumps as well, for your king of hearts will then score on the third round.

Using this method you will on balance break even with any sacrificers who lead a heart to the king on the first round, making a trick less than them when East has both honours and a trick more when West has them both. And you will be sure of a reasonable score when four spades is on.

Sacrifice

	♠ A K J 9				

♠ A K J 9
♡ 7 5 4
◇ 10 7 6 4 3
♣ 2

Game all. Dealer East

	West	North	East	South
			1 ♡	1 ♠
	3 ♣	4 ♠	—	—
	4 NT	—	5 ◇	—
	6 ♡	—	—	6 ♠
	Double	All pass		

♠ Q 10 8 7 5 2
♡ 3
◇ 2
♣ Q 8 6 4 3

West leads the ace of hearts against your doubled contract of six spades. He continues with the two of hearts and you ruff East's king. How should you plan the play?

This looks like a very good contract, for it appears certain that East would have made his slam. Not everyone will make a vulnerable overcall on your cards and it is likely that North and South will never get into the bidding at some tables. Nevertheless, there are sure to be some East-West pairs who don't bid the slam, and to outscore those who defend against a game contract you will want to hold your loss to 500, i.e. two down. This may be possible if the clubs break 4–3 and you are able to ruff three times in dummy.

It is fortunate that West did not lead a trump originally or switch to a trump at trick two. The opponents are sure to lead trumps when next they get in, and unhappily you will have to let them in twice—in clubs and diamonds—before you can establish the clubs.

If you lead a club now the opponent who wins will lead a trump, and when you later lead a diamond the defender who has a trump left will no doubt be able to win and lead his trump to make the penalty 800.

The proper procedure is to lead your diamond at trick three, win the trump return in dummy, and lead a club. The defender with the remaining trump may then be unable to obtain the lead. West might hold both ace and king of clubs and have no trump to return. Alternatively, East might slip up. If he has no more

176

trumps but holds the ace of clubs he might not care to duck the first club lead. Or, if he has the remaining trump, he could fail to go up with the king of clubs.

By leading the diamond first you give yourself a much improved chance of being able to establish your fifth club and thus hold the penalty to 500, which should be a magnificent score.

Let's see the full hand for a change.

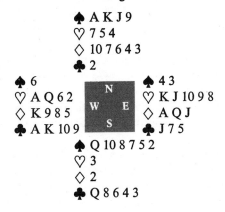

```
                    ♠ A K J 9
                    ♡ 7 5 4
                    ◇ 10 7 6 4 3
                    ♣ 2
        ♠ 6                        ♠ 4 3
        ♡ A Q 6 2        N         ♡ K J 10 9 8
        ◇ K 9 8 5    W       E     ◇ A Q J
        ♣ A K 10 9       S         ♣ J 7 5
                    ♠ Q 10 8 7 5 2
                    ♡ 3
                    ◇ 2
                    ♣ Q 8 6 4 3
```

12

Defence

DEFENDING against an enemy sacrifice can be a hazardous and frustrating affair. When you have the balance of strength it is annoying to hear the opponents blithely bidding on over your game call. In such cases the distribution is usually wild and your honour cards do not produce as many tricks in defence as you might hope.

Your decision to double rather than bid on may have been a very close one, but in conducting the defence you must always assume that it was correct. Act on the assumption that you have reached, if not beaten, par on the hand, for if you have slipped below par in the bidding you are not going to get many match-points anyway.

When the opponents by an unwise sacrifice have given you the chance of beating par, you must make sure that you exact the full penalty and outscore those who make game on your cards. When the opponents have reached a good sacrifice and landed in the par contract, on the other hand, you will have to be content with whatever penalty you can get. If the sacrifice was difficult to find you may not score well, but such reverses have to be accepted philosophically. They will be balanced by the occasions when your opponents fail to find a sacrifice that is reached at other tables.

Close partnership co-operation is often required in order to cash your tricks in the proper sequence. In defending against high-level contracts the margin for error is slender and a lost trick will usually mean disaster.

Defence

♠ K Q 7 4 3
♡ 2
◇ K Q J   *Love all*
♣ A 10 9 4   *Dealer West*

♠ 10 9   *West*   *North*   *East*   *South*
♡ A 9 7 6 5   1 ♡   Double   4 ♡   5 ◇
◇ A 9 4 3   Double   All pass
♣ K J

You lead the ten of spades against South's doubled contract of five diamonds. A low card is played from dummy, partner plays the ace, and declarer follows with the knave. East returns the knave of hearts, on which South plays the four. How do you plan the defence?

It looks as though partner has five hearts headed by the king, knave and ten, in which case eleven tricks in hearts are there for the taking, the only losers being a spade and a club. You will therefore need a penalty of 500 in order to outscore those who play in four or five hearts.

If South's knave of spades is a singleton your club trick cannot run away. You should therefore make sure of a second trump trick by overtaking the knave of hearts with your ace and forcing dummy to ruff by returning the suit. Don't make the mistake of leaving it to your partner, for he might have difficulty in reading the position. If East switched back to spades the declarer would discard his queen of hearts and escape for 300.

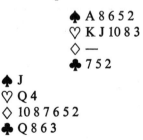

♠ A 8 6 5 2
♡ K J 10 8 3
◇ —
♣ 7 5 2

♠ J
♡ Q 4
◇ 10 8 7 6 5 2
♣ Q 8 6 3

179

Sacrifice

♠ 8
♡ A J 8 6
♦ K 10 8 3   *North-South game*
♣ A Q J 6   *Dealer West*

♠ A K 9 7 5 4 3   *West*
♡ 9 4
♦ 3
♣ K 9 4

West	North	East	South
1 ♠	Double	2 ♠	3 ♡
4 ♠	5 ♡	Double	All pass

You lead the singleton diamond and partner makes you happy by producing the ace, South following with the five. East returns the seven of diamonds and you ruff South's knave. How should you continue?

You could settle for one down by cashing a top spade, but if partner has the queen of spades you could boost the penalty to 500 by underleading your spade honours and getting another diamond ruff. Nothing much can be read into partner's non-committal seven of diamonds at the second trick. He would not consider possession of the queen of spades sufficient justification for leading his highest diamond.

A second look at the clubs in dummy should help to make up your mind. It looks as though the enemy would make three club tricks in defence, so unless your partner is void in hearts (unlikely on the bidding) you would not have made your contract of four spades.

The opponents have made a phantom sacrifice in that case, and any plus score you get is sure to be good. Don't be greedy, then. Just cash the ace of spades and accept your 200 with proper gratitude.

♠ J 10 2
♡ Q
♦ A 9 7 6 4
♣ 10 8 5 3

♠ Q 6
♡ K 10 7 5 3 2
♦ Q J 5
♣ 7 3

Defence

♠ J 9 6 4
♡ 8 7 4
Love all   ◇ Q
Dealer South   ♣ K Q 10 8 3

                            ♠ A K 5

South	West	North	East
2 ♠	Double	4 ♠	Double

                            ♡ 10 9 5 2

All pass   ◇ A 8 3
                             ♣ 7 6 5

North and South are using Tartan Two Bids, and the opening bid signifies a weak two-suited hand.

Partner leads the three of trumps and you play three rounds, West discarding the two of diamonds and the ace of hearts. The third round of trumps is won in dummy and the queen of diamonds led. You duck, but South overtakes with the king and continues with the knave of diamonds. Partner follows, a club is thrown from dummy and you take your ace. What do you lead now?

Partner's failure to echo in diamonds tells you that South has six of them. That means you can cash only two side-suit winners and will have to be content with 300. This seems to be the best you can do, for your limit is likely to be ten tricks in hearts and nine in no trumps (with six hearts West would surely have bid the suit rather than double).

To make sure of 300 you must give partner the information he needs to enable him to cash out. Lead the two of hearts to give him a count of the suit. If he started with five hearts he will know to cash the ace of clubs next, but if he started with only four hearts he will make a second trick in the suit.

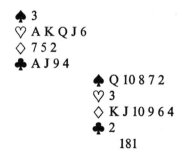

♠ 3
♡ A K Q J 6
◇ 7 5 2
♣ A J 9 4

        ♠ Q 10 8 7 2
        ♡ 3
        ◇ K J 10 9 6 4
        ♣ 2

Sacrifice

♠ 9 4
♡ J 7 6 3
◇ 9 6 5
♣ Q 8 5 2

East-West game
Dealer South

South	West	North	East
1 NT	—	—	Double
(12–14)			
All pass			

♠ Q J 3
♡ A 9 5
◇ A K J 7
♣ A 10 6

West leads the seven of spades to your knave and South plays the five. You continue with the queen of spades and South takes the ace, your partner following with the six. The declarer attacks clubs, playing the king and then the knave, and you hold up the ace until the third round, on which your partner throws the two of diamonds. How do you continue?

South has, in effect, sacrificed at the one-level against your game contract. It is all too apparent that you could have made either four spades or three no trumps, since partner is marked with a six-card spade suit. That means you will need a penalty of 800 to beat the East-West pairs who play in game. You can count five spade tricks, two diamonds, a heart and a club. The tenth defensive trick is still to be found.

If partner has the heart king all will be well, but he might have the queen. It is tempting to underlead the ace of hearts in order to give South an immediate guess, but on closer inspection the play is both dangerous and unnecessary. All you need do is cash the ace of hearts before putting partner in with the spade. This defensive Vienna Coup unblocks the heart menace and the run of the spades will squeeze South into submission.

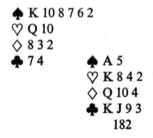

♠ K 10 8 7 6 2
♡ Q 10
◇ 8 3 2
♣ 7 4

♠ A 5
♡ K 8 4 2
◇ Q 10 4
♣ K J 9 3

182

Defence

♠ —
♡ 7 4
♢ K J 10 9 3   *East-West game*
♣ J 10 8 7 5 3   *Dealer East*

♠ A Q 5 2	*West*	*North*	*East*	*South*
♡ K J 9 5 3			3 ♠	—
♢ A Q	4 ♠	4 NT	—	5 ♣
♣ K Q	Double	All pass		

Your lead of the ace of spades is ruffed in dummy, partner playing the nine. South enters hand with the ace of clubs, ruffs another spade on the table, and leads the ten of clubs to which partner, surprisingly, follows. How do you continue?

Since East did not have great length in spades it is just possible that he has the ace of hearts. But to defend on this assumption would be the height of inconsistency. You assumed partner did not have the ace of hearts when you doubled five clubs instead of bidding on. You must continue to back the assumption that five clubs doubled is the par contract, and it is clear that you are not going to make more than three tricks in defence, a club, a diamond and a heart.

Should you play for partner to have the queen of hearts, then, and try to set up a heart trick before declarer can get the diamonds going? If you do a little counting you will realize that a heart lead would take an unnecessary risk. Declarer is marked with eight cards in the red suits and your heart trick can never disappear. Just play the ace and queen of diamonds and wait for the setting trick.

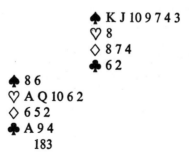

♠ K J 10 9 7 4 3
♡ 8
♢ 8 7 4
♣ 6 2

♠ 8 6
♡ A Q 10 6 2
♢ 6 5 2
♣ A 9 4

183

Sacrifice

			♠ 10 8 6 3	
			♡ K 7	
East-West game			◇ K 8 5 3	
Dealer East			♣ Q 10 4	
West	*North*	*East*	*South*	♠ 7
		1 ♡	1 ♠	♡ Q J 10 8 5 4
3 ♡	3 ♠	4 ♡	4 ♠	◇ A J
—	—	Double	All pass	♣ A 7 6 2

Your partner leads the ace of hearts on which you play the queen and South the three. West switches to the two of diamonds, a low card is played from dummy, and your knave wins the trick. How should you continue?

At this vulnerability your decision to double was a border-line one. It is more than likely that some players in your position will press on to five hearts. To score well you will therefore need a penalty of 800 if eleven tricks can be made in hearts.

Partner is marked with a high honour card in one of the black suits. If he has the ace of spades and a doubleton club five hearts will be on, but you will be unable to take more than 500 in defence. Forget about that possibility, since it would mean that you have fallen below par in the bidding. What else is there to go for?

West is not likely to have a singleton club or he would have switched to clubs at trick two in spite of your signal. The only other holding he could have which would allow five hearts to make is a doubleton king of clubs. That is the one to play for, since it gives you a chance of a 800 penalty by means of a ruff in each minor suit. You should therefore cash the ace of diamonds and then lead a small club.

This defence will net only 500 points when West has a small doubleton in one black suit and three to the king in the other. But in either of these cases ten tricks will be the limit in hearts and your score of 500 will at least beat those pairs who press on to five hearts.

184

Defence

The full hand:

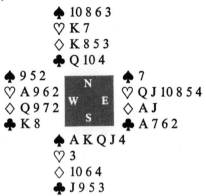

PART FIVE

Deception

13

Bidding

DECEPTIVE manœuvres in the bidding of a hand are normally dictated by tactical considerations. The good player bears in mind at all times that the main objective is to beat par. There are many different ways of achieving this end, and deceptive measures are more suited to some deals than to others. Each case has to be considered on its merits.

Kibitzers are occasionally surprised when their favourite expert fails to make the obvious value bid on a hand, particularly in competitive situations. Instead the expert may make a startling overbid, a gross underbid, or even a puzzling pass. If the kibitzer does not turn away in disgust, however, he will discover that the unorthodox action usually works out well in the end.

Tactical Overbids

There are two situations in which it can pay to overbid your values in competitive auctions. The first is when you are sure an enemy game is on. Then you will feel the urge to take pre-emptive action—to try to intimidate the enemy by a show of strength. An immediate jump to game may disguise your weakness, and you are certainly less likely to be doubled if you make your sacrifice in advance.

Deception

Love all. Dealer South

South	West	North	East
1 ♠	—	2 ♠	Double
?			

(a) ♠ A Q 10 7 4   (b) ♠ A Q 10 7 4
    ♡ 6   ♡ 6
    ◇ K Q J 6 2   ◇ K Q 7 6 2
    ♣ A 9   ♣ 9 4

With either of the above holdings South should bid four spades. On (a) he has the values for the bid and he expects to make his contract. On (b) he fully expects to go down, but he is less likely to be doubled if he bids an immediate four spades than if he eventually competes with four spades over an enemy game call of four hearts.

A player is best placed to make a deceptive advance sacrifice of this sort when his partner has limited his hand.

♠ 2   *East-West game. Dealer North*
♡ Q 10 9 6 5 4 2

	West	North	East	South
◇ 8 7 4		1 NT	—	?
♣ 5 3		(12–14)		

South can be sure of a good result by playing in hearts at any level up to four. He should therefore bid four hearts immediately rather than give West the chance to introduce spades or another suit at a lower level. The opponents are sure to credit South with more high-card strength than he has. Who knows, he may not even be doubled!

The other situation in which good players tend to make tactical overbids is when they do not really wish to play the hand at all but hope to induce the enemy to make a phantom sacrifice.

♠ J 10 8 3   *North-South game. Dealer South*
♡ A 10 7 5 4

	South	West	North	East
◇ A K 3	1 ♡	1 ♠	2 ♡	2 ♠
♣ 5	?			

Bidding

South does not have the values for more than a competitive raise to three hearts, but there is a lot to be said for a jump to four hearts. At this vulnerability the opponents may take the bid at its face value and go for the 'cheap' sacrifice in four spades.

Another instance:

♠ Q 10 9 3
♡ K 8 7 3   *North-South game. Dealer North*
♢ Q 10 5 2   *West*   *North*   *East*   *South*
♣ 6   1 ♡   Double   ?

The book bid after the double is three hearts, but a jump to four hearts has an excellent chance of inducing a phantom sacrifice by opponents.

This technique, known in the vernacular as 'bumping', should not be applied indiscriminately. It is obviously a great advantage to know the opposition. We all know opponents who will never fail to make a phantom sacrifice in such circumstances.

Tactical Underbids

When a player wishes to conceal the full playing strength of his hand, he can usually best do so by resorting to a slight underbid.

♠ 6
♡ —   *Love all. Dealer North*
♢ K 10 7 4 3   *West*   *North*   *East*   *South*
♣ A K 9 8 7 3 2   3 ♢   Double   ?

With the above hand your main concern should be to win the declaration at all costs. You can be fairly sure of making twelve tricks in diamonds (perhaps thirteen if spades are not led), but it is clear that the opponents must have a cheap sacrifice against six diamonds. If you show too much confidence by leaping to six diamonds the opponents may bid out of fright. The best chance of getting to play the hand lies in underbidding slightly on the first round. Try jumping to five diamonds. When you later come in with six diamonds over the enemy five spades or five hearts, they may think you are sacrificing and double you.

Deception

It is necessary to produce a sequence that is plausible, otherwise the opponents will smell a rat. To pass on the first round, or to bid only four diamonds, would be overdoing things. The enemy would ask themselves what sort of a hand can pass and then come in at the six-level, and they would probably reach the right conclusion. Slight underbidding, with the emphasis on the 'slight', is the way to ensure plausibility.

Use can often be made of the forcing pass to create an impression of uncertainty. If you appear to be unsure of what you are doing the opponents are more likely to allow you to play the hand.

<table>
<tr><td></td><td colspan="4">North-South game. Dealer South</td></tr>
<tr><td>♠ —</td><td>South</td><td>West</td><td>North</td><td>East</td></tr>
<tr><td>♡ A 10 9 7 4</td><td>2 ♣</td><td>3 ♠</td><td>—</td><td>4 ♠</td></tr>
<tr><td>◇ A K Q J 6</td><td>—</td><td>—</td><td>5 ♡</td><td>5 ♠</td></tr>
<tr><td>♣ A K 3</td><td>?</td><td></td><td></td><td></td></tr>
</table>

Partner has hit the jackpot with his heart response. A small slam is sure to be on, and there could even be seven if partner has the right cards. You could now bid five no trumps as a grand slam force, telling partner to bid seven if he has the king and queen of hearts.

However, if you bid as confidently as that it is highly improbable that you will be allowed to play the hand either in seven hearts or in six. The par contract on this hand is sure to be six or seven spades doubled, and you will beat par handsomely if you can persuade the opponents to let you play in hearts at the six-level.

The best way of trying to achieve this is to pass, as though uncertain of your best course of action. The pass is forcing on your partner, of course, but he is unlikely to wish to bid again at the six-level. He will therefore almost certainly double. You can then take out the double into six hearts, and the opponents may be sufficiently unsure of the position to allow you to play there.

There is one old chestnut, discussed many times in print, which makes an appearance at the bridge table only when there is a practical joker around. What do you open if you are dealt thirteen of a suit?

Bidding

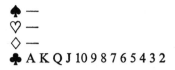

♠ —
♡ —
♢ —
♣ A K Q J 10 9 8 7 6 5 4 3 2

There is certainly a case to be made out for a tactical underbid of five or six clubs. It is quite likely that the opponents will compete, and when you later 'sacrifice' in seven clubs you may be allowed to play there. An alternative opening bid is four no trumps, but if you happen to find partner with three aces how will you restrain him from bidding seven no trumps over your seven clubs? That contract is not likely to be a success.

Practical pairs players will open with the obvious bid of seven clubs. The other hands may well be so distributed that neither opponent can see a profitable sacrifice, and even if they can you will be far from alone in the result you obtain.

Inhibitory Bids

In every rubber bridge school there is one happy-go-lucky character who likes to open the bidding in his shortest suit and then bounce to three no trumps when his partner raises. He enjoys an occasional success, usually when the left-hand opponent is a stranger unacquainted with his style. But for tournament bridge, where it is important to maintain partnership confidence at all times, such extreme tactics cannot be seriously considered.

There are, however, plenty of opportunities for leading the enemy astray. It is in the field of trial and cue bidding that the most fruitful ground for deception is to be found. Trial bids are usually made in suits where you require a little help from partner if game is to be a worth-while proposition. When you need honest information from partner you must, of course, make an honest trial bid. But there will be many occasions when you require no further information from partner, having the values for game in your own hand. At such times it can be profitable to indulge in a piece of misdirection.

Deception

♠ 7 6 2
♡ A Q J 8 4
♢ A K J 6 2
♣ —

South	North
1 ♡	2 ♡
?	

You have the values to jump straight to game, but a false trial bid of two spades is unlikely to do any harm and may well inhibit a spade lead.

Perhaps you and your partner have agreed to play short-suit trial bids. An agreement with partner does not, of course, constitute an undertaking to the opponents, and there is no reason at all why you should not depart from your normal practice whenever you see a possible advantage in so doing.

Love all

Dealer South

♠ K J 10 7 2
♡ A Q 5
♢ 7
♣ A K 10 9

South	North
1 ♠	2 ♠
?	

The short suit trial bid would be three diamonds, but here there is not the slightest need to make a trial bid since you are quite prepared to play in game opposite the barest of minimum raises. Instead of going direct to four spades, however, you could first trail a red herring with a bid of three hearts.

Even if this does not induce a heart lead it may create a little confusion in the minds of your opponents. Their uncertainty about your distribution could work to your advantage in the later play.

The picture should not be painted with too heavy a brush. The advantage lies not so much in making false trial bids as in gaining a reputation for doing so. To keep the opponents on the wrong foot you have to mix your shots skilfully. An occasional fake trial bid interspersed with your genuine ones will act like a well-disguised lob after a series of hard drives. Aim to keep the enemy in perpetual doubt about the honesty of your bids. That is sure to be worth a lot of tricks to you in the long run.

Bidding

Cue bidding offers still further scope for players with larcenous instincts. Here is an amusing deal on which North and South were convincingly talked out of a cold grand slam.

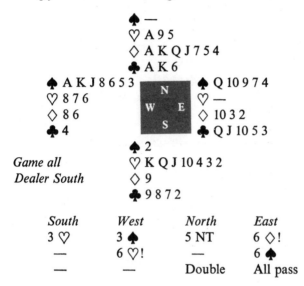

```
                    ♠ —
                    ♡ A 9 5
                    ◇ A K Q J 7 5 4
                    ♣ A K 6
   ♠ A K J 8 6 5 3                    ♠ Q 10 9 7 4
   ♡ 8 7 6              N              ♡ —
   ◇ 8 6            W       E          ◇ 10 3 2
   ♣ 4                  S              ♣ Q J 10 5 3
                    ♠ 2
   Game all         ♡ K Q J 10 4 3 2
   Dealer South     ◇ 9
                    ♣ 9 8 7 2
```

South	West	North	East
3 ♡	3 ♠	5 NT	6 ◇ !
—	6 ♡ !	—	6 ♠
—	—	Double	All pass

East considered the possession of three cards in the suit quite insufficient reason to refrain from showing a void in diamonds. This made it dangerous for South to make the proper response of seven hearts to his partner's grand slam force. Instead he decided to pass in the hope that this would convey the right message.

West was uncertain of what was going on. It seemed unlikely that his partner had a genuine diamond suit, or that he was void. West eventually made the happy decision to add to the confusion with a bid of six hearts.

Now North was on the spot. With West void in hearts and East void in diamonds it seemed that no grand slam could be made, and so he passed in the hope of collecting 1,200. East converted to six spades, however, and North and South had to be content with a penalty of 500.

Par was assassinated by the false cue bids and East and West

Deception

earned themselves a clear top, since no other pair conceded less than 800.

It is sometimes possible to play upon the opponents' fears in a similar fashion by the use of a false Lightner double.

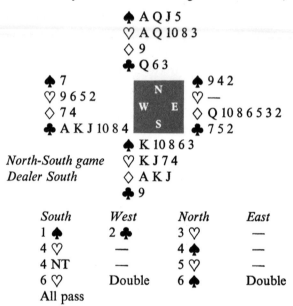

```
                    ♠ A Q J 5
                    ♡ A Q 10 8 3
                    ◇ 9
                    ♣ Q 6 3
        ♠ 7                         ♠ 9 4 2
        ♡ 9 6 5 2          N        ♡ —
        ◇ 7 4          W       E    ◇ Q 10 8 6 5 3 2
        ♣ A K J 10 8 4     S        ♣ 7 5 2
                    ♠ K 10 8 6 3
North-South game    ♡ K J 7 4
Dealer South        ◇ A K J
                    ♣ 9
```

South	West	North	East
1 ♠	2 ♣	3 ♡	—
4 ♡	—	4 ♠	—
4 NT	—	5 ♡	—
6 ♡	Double	6 ♠	Double
All pass			

When South bid six hearts West felt hard done by. Not only had the opponents reached a slam but they appeared to have bid it in the right suit. Knowing that his partner was likely to be void in hearts on this bidding, West doubled to suggest that he was void in spades.

Who can blame North for taking the double at its face value and converting to spades? This assured East and West of a good score. Plus 500 was, in fact, a shared top.

A manœuvre that hardly deserves to succeed but sometimes does is the psychic five-level double.

196

Bidding

♠ 10 8 5 2				*North-South game. Dealer North*
♡ Q 10 3		*West*	*North*	*East*	*South*
◇ 8			3 ♠	Double	—
♣ 10 7 6 5 3		4 ♣	—	5 ♡	?

If you pass it is long odds that West will press on to six hearts, and a sacrifice in six spades could be too expensive. If you are confident enough that your partner will not have an outside trick, this is a good moment to try a double.

John Lowenthal of Pittsburg has aptly named this the Striped-Tail Ape Double, for if either opponent redoubles you will have to turn tail like the cowardly ape and flee for the shelter of five spades.

The full hand might be:

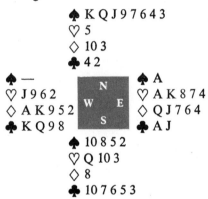

```
              ♠ K Q J 9 7 6 4 3
              ♡ 5
              ◇ 10 3
              ♣ 4 2
♠ —                        ♠ A
♡ J 9 6 2        N         ♡ A K 8 7 4
◇ A K 9 5 2   W     E      ◇ Q J 7 6 4
♣ K Q 9 8        S         ♣ A J
              ♠ 10 8 5 2
              ♡ Q 10 3
              ◇ 8
              ♣ 10 7 6 5 3
```

If neither opponent is sufficiently confident to redouble you will score well, for one overtrick in five hearts doubled will give the enemy only 750 points.

Psychic Bids

Players who indulge in psychic bidding on completely worthless hands do not get very far in the pairs game. The psychic bid is better reserved for a surprise injection into a team game, where it may succeed in creating a large swing. At pairs it tends to produce

Deception

bottom scores more often than tops and it has a deplorable effect on partnership confidence. You would therefore be justified in resorting to an out-and-out psyche only if you were desperate for tops.

Semi-psychic bids when partner has passed are another matter. Third in hand, not vulnerable against vulnerable opponents, you are ideally placed for semi-psychic adventures, which can turn out to be very profitable. How flimsy an opening has to be before it ceases to be a light opening bid and becomes a psychic bid is a matter for conjecture.

♠ J 10 7 4				
♡ A Q 10 6 4	*East-West game. Dealer North*			
◇ 8 3	*West*	*North*	*East*	*South*
♣ 9 2	—	—		?

Most experienced pairs players will be with me in opening one heart with the above hand, whether they call it a light opening or a lead-directing psyche. Lead-direction should always be one of the aims of such bids, certainly. Also worth noting is the four-card spade holding which tips the balance in favour of bidding rather than passing.

When you have made a semi-psychic opening it is important to follow it up intelligently in the later bidding.

♠ A J 9 6 4 3	*East-West game. Dealer North*			
♡ 9 8 4	*West*	*North*	*East*	*South*
◇ 7 5		—	—	1 ♠
♣ 10 3	Double	3 ♠	4 ♡	?

Partner's double raise after the double shows a weak distributional hand and it is therefore quite possible that the opponents can make a slam. There sure to be a worth-while sacrifice in spades at the four- or five-level, but your chance of being allowed to play in four spades is negligible. You could try a direct bid of five spades or a cheeky one of four no trumps, but you are unlikely to convince the enemy that their aces and kings are a mirage. Perhaps the best answer is once again the deceptive cue-bid. If

Bidding

you bid five clubs or five diamonds over four hearts the opponents, fearing that you can get a ruff, may permit you to play in five spades doubled.

Another useful type of semi-psychic is the third-in-hand bid of a three-card suit on a balanced ten or eleven points.

(a) ♠ K J 3   (b) ♠ Q 7 6 2
    ♡ J 7 6 4   ♡ A 9 5
    ♢ A Q 6   ♢ J 10 4 2
    ♣ 9 8 5   ♣ K 5

At favourable vulnerability a bid of one spade on (a) and one heart on (b) is unlikely to come to much harm, for you are prepared to pass any response by your partner.

Such bids may steal the opponents' suit and jostle them into an inferior contract.

14

Dummy Play

ONE of the most useful attributes a pairs player can acquire is a deceptive style when playing the dummy. The expert's advantage is at its greatest in this facet of the game, and it is here that the average player will find the most scope for rapid progress. A little serious study will be rewarded by large numbers of match-points.

What constitutes a deceptive style? Basically it is just a matter of concealing your assets and your liabilities from the defenders for as long as possible. There are a hundred small ways in which this may be achieved. Some of them are well known, but there are others which never occur to the majority of players.

The essence of deception is, of course, smoothness. The confidence trickster who stammers when he tells a lie will never have much success in his vocation. It is important to maintain the same even tempo in your play whether you are making the normal, technically correct play or attempting an outrageous bluff. For this reason it is advisable to study in advance the various situations that may arise so that you will know how to deal with them at the table.

The declarer has an advantage over the defenders in that he does not have to feed information to his partner in the play of the

Dummy Play

hand. Dummy is *hors de combat* for the duration of the play and you can select your cards to cause the maximum confusion in the enemy ranks. In winning a trick you will often have a choice of honour cards and in following suit a choice of small cards to play. In such situations you can exploit your flair for larceny to the full. The card to play is the one that will be ambiguous from the defenders' point of view. It will often be possible for you to suggest a switch when this is what you want and to induce a continuation when this will suit your ends.

Most declarers know what to do when West leads a suit in which they hold ace, king and another and East plays the queen. If the contract is no trumps they win with the king so as to give East the impression that his partner may be able to take the rest of the tricks in the suit. In a suit contract, on the other hand, they win with the ace in order to leave open for West the possibility that his partner may have the king.

x x x

A Q J

Similarly, with the above holding, when West leads small and East plays the ten most players are subtle enough to win with the queen, leaving West guessing about the location of the knave.

J 10 x

A Q 9

In the above situation the most deceptive play is to put up dummy's knave as though trying to induce a cover and overtake with the queen when East plays low. This can be very convincing if you then use an outside entry in dummy in order to finesse towards West in another suit. If the finesse loses, West is likely to continue his attack, expecting your ace to fall.

x x x

K Q x

When West leads a low card and East plays the knave, the

Deception

proper card to win the trick with is the king. West may then place his partner with the queen and lead the suit again when he gets in.

<table>
<tr><td>(a)</td><td>A</td><td>(b)</td><td>A</td></tr>
<tr><td></td><td>Q 10 9 x x x x</td><td></td><td>Q J 10 x x x x</td></tr>
</table>

Suppose that in each case this is the trump suit and that both opponents follow with small cards on the first round. Which card should you lead on the second round?

Technically there is no difference. In case (a) there is an equal likelihood that an opponent will hold a doubleton king or a doubleton knave. Psychologically the lead of the queen has a slight edge, however, for if it transpires that you have two trump losers only one opponent will know about it. The other will be kept guessing about the length and strength of your trump suit, and this may affect his defence. You should, of course, make exactly the same play in case (b), leading the queen on the second round instead of the lazy ten.

It is only a small point, but a hundred small points like that add up to a deceptive style. The next diagram illustrates the same principle.

<table>
<tr><td>(c)</td><td>—</td><td>(d)</td><td>—</td></tr>
<tr><td></td><td>A K J 9 x x x</td><td></td><td>A K J 10 x x x</td></tr>
</table>

Again, if opponents follow low to the first two rounds you should continue with the knave in both cases.

In all the examples considered so far it has been the higher card that is the more deceptive, but this is not always the case. It depends on what you are trying to achieve.

K 7 5 2

Q J 10

The above is a side suit in a trump contract and West leads the three, an obvious singleton. Here the middle card is the one to create ambiguity and you should have your knave ready to drop

Dummy Play

under the ace. The knave is the only card which, from East's point of view, could be single in your hand. West would not lead the three from Q J 3 or J 10 3, but he would from Q 10 3.

                    K 7 5 2
        3 led
                    J 10 9

Similarly, with the above holding you must smoothly drop the ten under the ace to create ambiguity for East.

    (a) Q 8 3   (b) K 7 5

        A 10 9   J 10

The above holdings again represent side suits in a trump contract. In (a) if you have to lead from hand the best card is the nine, concealing from West that you have a choice of plays. Holding the king, West is less likely to duck if you lead the nine. If he does play low, therefore, your best chance will be to run the nine.

On (b) most players would lead the knave and watch West's reactions, but unless West is a novice he will just play a low card with a poker face and leave you with the guess. If you are marked with shortage in the suit it will normally be better to lead the ten. West may think you have no alternative to going up with the king in dummy, and he will be less likely to duck if he has the ace.

Note the difference between the next two examples.

    (a) A 7 4   (b) A 7 4 2

        Q J 9   Q J 10 6

In (a) you wish to induce an immediate cover from West and the best chance lies in leading the queen. No doubt West should not cover unless he also holds the ten, but players often do.

In (b) you intend to finesse but do not need a cover on the first round. The proper card to lead is therefore the ten. West will not cover the ten with a guarded king. If he does play the

Deception

king on the first round there is a fair inference that it was single and you should take the deep finesse on the way back.

Choosing the correct honour card to play, while important, is not enough to make you a tricky declarer. The expert achieves most of his deceptive effects by the manner in which he handles his small cards.

Most players are aware of the possibility of confusing the enemy signals in situations like the following.

Q 7 2

A K J 9 4   10 8 6

5 3

When West leads the ace or king you drop the five. If West thinks his partner is echoing to show a doubleton he will continue the suit to your advantage.

The opposite situation arises in the next diagram.

Q 7 2

A K J 9 8   5

10 6 4 3

Now you must drop the three on the first round in order to leave open for West the possibility that his partner started with 10 6 5.

The rule for echoing in such situations is the same for declarer as for the defenders—echo when you want a continuation and play low when you want a switch.

7 6 3

K led   8 played

Q 10 5 2

At no trumps, your play of the five on the first trick may persuade West that he has struck oil.

It is not only in following suit that you should select your small cards with care; the cards you lead are equally important. Defenders who echo to show distribution are particularly vulnerable to this sort of signal-scrambling.

Dummy Play

K Q 10 9

J 6 2

Playing in a no-trump contract with no side entry in dummy, you would like the opponents to take the ace on the second round. How you set about the suit will depend on which defender you think has the ace, for the second lead of the suit must come through him.

If you believe West to have the ace, lead the knave and continue with the six. By concealing the two you may persuade West that his partner is echoing to show four cards in the suit, and he may see no point in holding up the ace again. For the deception to have a chance West must be made to play ahead of his partner, because East's second card will expose the position.

If you decide to play East for the ace you must tackle the suit differently. Lead the six on the first round and 'finesse' dummy's nine, then continue with the king from the table. If East, holding A x x, is persuaded that his partner has J x x x he may take the ace on the second round.

Concealing a low card may pay dividends in a suit contract as well.

K Q 10 8

J 9 5   A 7 4 2

6 3

If you lead the six to dummy's queen, East may be unwilling to hold off lest his partner is signalling to show four cards in the suit. It is always helpful if you can persuade opponents to take their aces on the first round. This clarifies the position for you and makes the subsequent play easier.

Often you will be able to create the impression that you are taking a finesse. You should normally try to do this as a matter of routine.

(a) A Q J 7   (b) A Q 8 4

K 4 3   K 7 2

Deception

In (*a*) if you wish to enter dummy in order to lead another suit, don't tip your hand by using the ace. Lead the four to dummy's knave. West may think his partner is holding up and echoing, while East may receive the impression that his partner has the king and may therefore place you with cards you do not possess in other suits. In (*b*) lead the seven and 'finesse' dummy's queen. West cannot be deceived this time, but if East has J x x x he may eventually discard in the suit in the belief that his partner has the king.

When leading from dummy towards honours in your own hand there is no possibility of scrambling the signals, but it may still be possible to conceal your strength in the suit.

K 7 3

10 9 5   J 8 6

A Q 4 2

If you lead the three from dummy and win with the queen, West may receive the impression that his partner has the ace. On gaining the lead he may attack the suit and present you with a tempo.

8 5

A K Q J

Playing in a suit contract, you may wish to get a discard in dummy on this suit before drawing trumps. Just in case West has a doubleton in the suit you should lead from dummy, 'finesse' the queen, and continue with the ace followed by the knave. This costs nothing, and if West believes his partner to have the king you will get your discard.

K J 10 4

A Q 5

With the above holding you may need a discard in your own hand while there are still trumps out. If dummy has outside entries the best plan is to lead the ace and continue with the five to dummy's king. Then lead the knave from the table and East if he is now void may decline to ruff, placing his partner with the queen.

In going from hand to hand the expert seldom misses a chance to sow a little confusion in the enemy ranks.

A K 6

Q 4 2

Crossing to dummy in this suit you should lead the four rather than the two, particularly if you are fearful of an attack in another suit. Each defender may believe the other to be echoing and may lead the suit when he gets in.

There are many situations in which a ducking play will be the best method of concealing your strength, especially when this can be combined with a spot of signal-scrambling. By reticent play in the early stages of a hand you can often make it very difficult for the opponents to tell exactly what is going on.

Concealing weaknesses may be more difficult, but in general the reverse principle applies. By playing your highest card in the weak suit you can often give the impression of strength and induce the defenders to switch.

9 6 4

Q 7

If East leads a low card in this suit there is nothing to be lost by playing the queen. This may give West the idea that you are well upholstered in the suit and persuade him to try something else.

Quite apart from the deceptive angle there are sound technical reasons for playing your highest card from a worthless holding when the suit is led by your right-hand opponent. By playing high you may create severe communication problems for the defenders.

Deception

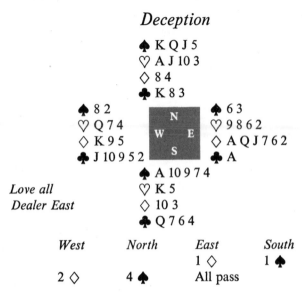

♠ K Q J 5
♡ A J 10 3
◇ 8 4
♣ K 8 3

♠ 8 2
♡ Q 7 4
◇ K 9 5
♣ J 10 9 5 2

♠ 6 3
♡ 9 8 6 2
◇ A Q J 7 6 2
♣ A

♠ A 10 9 7 4
♡ K 5
◇ 10 3
♣ Q 7 6 4

Love all
Dealer East

West	*North*	*East*	*South*
		1 ◇	1 ♠
2 ◇	4 ♠	All pass	

West leads the knave of clubs against your four-spade contract. East wins with the ace and returns the two of diamonds.

First, see what happens if you play the three of diamonds. West wins with the nine and returns the two of clubs for his partner to ruff. East underleads his ace of diamonds again and gets another club ruff to put you two down. This will be a bad result, for not all the West players will find that devilish club lead.

Note the difference if you play the ten on the first round of diamonds. West has to play the king and the defence is no longer clear-cut. West will not imagine his nine of diamonds to be a second entry and will probably lead the nine of clubs for East to ruff. Even if West does lead the two of clubs it will require nerves of steel for East to underlead his diamond honours again. In practice you are almost certain to get out for one down, which will tie with all the declarers who had a small diamond led against them originally.

When the hand was played in a tournament one down was worth seven match-points out of twelve, but two down scored only two.

Dummy Play

♠ Q 2
♡ K Q 7 6 3
◇ K 10 6 4
♣ 9 3

Game all
Dealer South

South	North
1 ♣	1 ♡
3 ♣	3 ◇
3 NT	—

♠ 10 6 4
♡ 8
◇ A J 3
♣ A K Q J 7 2

West leads the three of spades against your three no trump contract. How do you plan the play?

Your gamble looks like failing, but the hand is not over yet. On such occasions it is important to recognize what your chances are and make the most of them. Here you have two faint hopes. West may have led away from the ace and king of spades. Alternatively he may, with a little help, misread the spade situation.

You should play the queen of spades from the table and smoothly drop the six under East's king. When East returns the five of spades you play the ten. West wins with the knave and goes into a trance. Can you see what he is thinking about?

Now your foresight may be about to pay off, for West must have A 8 of spades left and is wondering if you started with 10 9 7 6 and his partner with K 5 4. If he concludes that this is the case he will try to find his partner's entry card so that he can get another spade lead through. He has only to lead the wrong red suit and you will have brought home an impossible contract and beaten par by a mile.

That ten of spades at trick two will seldom deceive an expert West. He will reason that with 10 9 7 6 opposite Q 2 declarer would make certain of stopping the spades by playing low from dummy at trick one. But even experts nod sometimes. And not every West is an expert.

Confusion normally works for declarer. With no partner to mislead, he should give defenders the maximum opportunity to go astray. If they are forced to guess, they will sometimes misguess—especially if the odds are stacked against them.

Deception

♠ 10 7 6 5 3
♡ 10 6 4
♢ 10
♣ A 6 5 2

Game all. Dealer South

South	West	North	East
1 ♠	—	2 ♠	—
—	Double	3 ♠	All pass

♠ A Q J 9
♡ K 8 2
♢ K Q 3
♣ J 8 3

You play in three spades after a typical match-point auction, and West leads the king of clubs. You play the two from dummy and the eight from hand, East following with the four. West doesn't fall for that one but switches to the four of trumps. You put up the ten, East plays low, and you drop the nine. When you lead another trump and finesse the knave, West discards the seven of hearts. Your ace of trumps fells the king while West completes an echo with the five of hearts. How should you continue?

It looks as though East has the ace of diamonds. If you lead a diamond from hand at this stage you will therefore go one down in your contract. This may not be at all bad, for it is clear that the opponents could make a three-diamond contract, losing only a spade, two diamonds and a club. They have already fallen below par by failing to double three spades.

However, it would be better still to make your contract, and your small deception in clubs has left you ideally placed to put West on the guessing griddle. Lead the knave of clubs and duck again when West covers.

West will have a tough decision to make. For all he knows you could have the ace of diamonds and his partner king and another heart. In that case a heart switch would be mandatory in order that the defence could cash three heart tricks before one of your losing hearts could be discarded on dummy's fourth club. If West does lead a heart you will beat par handsomely by making nine tricks.

Manufacturing an echo may be all that is required to put the defenders on the wrong track.

Dummy Play

♠ A 2
♡ 9 8 5 3
◇ K J 7 3   *North-South game*
♣ A 9 7   *Dealer South*

                  South   *North*

♠ K 6 3   1 ♡   4 ◇ (Swiss)
♡ K J 10 7 2   4 ♡   —
◇ A Q 8
♣ 8 4

West leads the knave of spades against your four heart contract. How do you plan the play?

You should, of course, win with the ace, dropping the six from
your hand as a matter of routine, and lead a trump. The full
hand may be as follows.

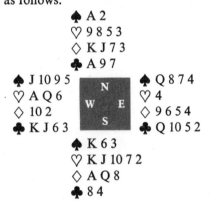

                ♠ A 2
                ♡ 9 8 5 3
                ◇ K J 7 3
                ♣ A 9 7

♠ J 10 9 5   ♠ Q 8 7 4
♡ A Q 6   ♡ 4
◇ 10 2   ◇ 9 6 5 4
♣ K J 6 3   ♣ Q 10 5 2

                ♠ K 6 3
                ♡ K J 10 7 2
                ◇ A Q 8
                ♣ 8 4

You are safe for eleven tricks provided that West does not find
the club switch when in with the queen of hearts. It will be very
difficult for him to switch if he thinks his partner is encouraging
in spades. The most natural thing in the world for West will be to
lead a spade to his partner's imagined king in the hope of getting
a club return before his ace of trumps can be knocked out.

Deception

♠ 7 4
♡ K J 3
◇ J 9
♣ A 9 8 6 5 3

♠ A Q 5
♡ A Q 9 6 4
◇ Q 4 2
♣ K 7

Love all. Dealer South

South	West	North	East
1 ♡	1 ♠	2 ♣	—
3 NT	All pass		

Against your three no trump contract West leads the ten of spades and East plays the knave, which you take with your queen. How do you plan the play?

Nine tricks are assured and this is just a matter of overtricks. On the normal 3–2 break dummy's club suit will provide overtricks galore, but if the opponents recognize the danger they will cash three fast tricks.

The best method of tackling the hand is to lead the seven of clubs and duck in dummy, conceding the club loser at the earliest possible moment. No matter which defender wins this trick, he is unlikely to make any play but the natural one of a spade continuation. This is just what you want, of course. With clubs breaking evenly you will have twelve tricks and an excellent score.

To have cashed the top clubs before conceding the loser would have made the situation very clear to the defenders. One of them would have the opportunity to signal in diamonds, but even without a signal they would surely recognize the danger of allowing you to make overtricks and cash what tricks they could in the diamond suit.

Situations such as this are quite common, and subtle play is required to conceal from the defenders their urgent need to cash out.

Dummy Play

♠ A 7 6 3
♡ A K
◇ A Q 5
♣ K 10 7 4

Game all
Dealer North

♠ K
♡ Q 9 8 7 6 4 3 2
◇ J 3
♣ 9 5

North	South
2 NT	4 ♡

West leads the four of diamonds against your four heart contract. How do you plan the play?

If West has led away from the king you can make all thirteen tricks by running the lead round to your knave. But players also lead from four to the ten. If East has the king of diamonds he is likely to switch to clubs and hold you to eleven tricks. Then perhaps you should rely on West for the ace of clubs, going up with the ace of diamonds and discarding your second diamond on the ace of spades.

The diamond lead has really put you at a bit of a disadvantage. Anyone who receives a spade or trump lead will have time to discard a club on the ace of spades and then try first the clubs and then the diamonds in search of the twelfth trick.

On the whole it seems best to take the immediate diamond finesse, but by reducing your chance of thirteen tricks you can improve the likelihood of making twelve, which should be a good enough score. Play the queen of diamonds from dummy at trick one. If East wins he will then be more likely to return the suit, particularly if he has the ace of clubs. If he does return a diamond you will eventually get both your clubs away on dummy's winners.

And if the queen of diamonds wins the first trick you will still have squeeze possibilities for the thirteenth trick.

Deception

♠ 9 8 5 3
♡ A 6 4
◇ K J
♣ K 7 6 2

Love all
Dealer South

	South	North
♠ A K Q J 2	1 ♠	3 ♠
♡ K 10 9	4 ♠	—
◇ 7 6 4		
♣ Q 5		

West leads the two of diamonds against your four spade contract. The knave draws the ace and East returns the eight of hearts which is covered by the ten, knave and ace. On a club lead from dummy your queen scores, and when you test the trumps they prove to be 2–2. How should you continue?

It appears that West has the queen of hearts and East the ace of clubs. The only legitimate chance of an overtrick is that East started with just three clubs, in which case you will be able to establish dummy's king for a heart discard.

Many players would see nothing better to do than lead their second club and duck in dummy, but this is a poor effort. East may not know that your second club is a small one. Why make life easy for him by tipping your hand? There are plenty of entries in dummy and the proper play is to go in with the king of diamonds and lead the second club from the table.

If East does not have the knave of clubs he will have a problem, even if he has four cards in the suit. For all he knows your second club may be the knave, in which case he ought to go up with the ace and shoot another heart through to give his partner what tricks he can take in the suit.

By leading from dummy you increase your chances quite a lot, and it is the mark of the good declarer that he never misses an opportunity of giving a defender a guess like this.

Dummy Play

Although your normal aim will be to conceal your holdings from the enemy, there are occasions when it pays to make sure that a defender knows exactly what you hold in a certain suit.

♠ A K		
♡ Q 7 2		
♢ K Q J 10 7 3	*North-South game*	
♣ 8 3	*Dealer North*	
	North	*South*
♠ Q 9 6 4	1 ♢	1 ♠
♡ K J	3 ♢	3 NT
♢ 6 5 2		
♣ K Q J 9		

West leads the three of hearts against your contract of three no trumps and East plays the ace. How do you like that?

You don't like it, of course. The defenders have found the only attack that will hold you to nine tricks, for they will establish a long heart before you can knock out both minor suit aces. The blockage in spades unfortunately prevents you from scoring the spade queen as a tenth trick.

You will still make ten tricks if you can persuade East to switch, however, and the best way of doing that is to drop your king of hearts under the ace. Since his partner's lead gives him a count of the suit, East will know that you have the knave of hearts as well, and he may regard your play of the king as a clumsy attempt to get him to continue hearts.

A club switch may look quite attractive to East, particularly if he has the ace of diamonds but not the ace of clubs. Note that if you held the club ace instead of the king and queen a club switch would be East's only correct play.

The club switch might come even if you play the knave of hearts on the first trick, but it is more likely if you play the king.

Deception

♠ Q 6 3
♡ A K 7 2
◇ J 10
♣ Q 7 6 3

North-South game. Dealer West

West	North	East	South
3 ♡	—	—	3 ♠
—	4 ♠	All pass	

♠ A K 9 8 2
♡ 4
◇ K Q 9 8 3
♣ K 5

West leads the queen of hearts against your four spade contract. You put on the ace and, to your relief, East follows with the eight. How should you continue?

It looks like an overtrick all the way unless you run into a bad trump break. On the bidding it is quite likely that East will have long trumps, but you would hardly dare to risk a deep finesse of the nine if West follows to the first round with a small trump.

What you can do, however, is give East an opportunity to disclose the position at trick two. Lead out the king of hearts and watch his reactions. He cannot know that a discard will be of no use to you and if he has two or three trumps he will surely play one without hesitation.

If East plays a trump honour after a trance you should play him for four trumps by over-ruffing, leading a trump to the queen and finessing on the way back. You should also play him for four trumps if he discards on the king of hearts. Discard your small club, cash the queen of spades, then take the deep finesse. East may split his honours, but you can re-enter dummy in diamonds to finesse again in trumps. The most awkward defence will be if East discards a diamond on the king of hearts and West wins the first round of diamonds and leads a heart to let East discard another diamond. On ruffing this, however, you can safely lead the king of clubs. West cannot have both minor aces, and when East takes the ace of clubs he will have to put you back in dummy which will enable you to take another trump finesse.

Dummy Play

Most players would instinctively do the right thing in the following case.

♠ J 7		
♡ A J 9 6 2		
◇ K Q 8 6 5	*Game all*	
♣ Q	*Dealer North*	
	North	*South*
♠ Q 9 8 6 4 3	1 ♡	1 ♠
♡ 7	2 ◇	2 ♠
◇ 4 2		
♣ K J 10 5		

West leads the king of hearts against your two spade contract and you win with dummy's ace. How should you continue?

This looks like a sure eight tricks, for at most you will lose three spades and the minor suit aces. There is, moreover, a chance of an overtrick if you can locate the ten of spades. Which way do you choose to finesse in trumps?

The answer should be neither way, for the time being. Why risk a finesse in trumps when there is a good chance of inducing the opponents to do the work for you? If you can persuade them to lead trumps all guesswork will be eliminated.

The proper play is to lead the queen of clubs at the second trick. The defender who wins with the ace will be sorely tempted, even without an echo in clubs from his partner, to lead trumps in an effort to remove all ruffing values from dummy.

And that is likely to give you an easy overtrick.

Deception

♠ J 10 6 2
♡ 10 5
♢ Q 7 4
♣ A 7 6 5

	Game all
	Dealer South
South	North
1 ♠	2 ♠
4 ♠	—

♠ A K 8 5 4
♡ A J 3
♢ K 10
♣ K J 2

Against your four-spade contract West leads the king of hearts and you win with the ace. When you play out the top trumps the queen drops doubleton on your left. How should you continue?

Perhaps by now you are wishing that you had said three no trumps on the second round instead of four spades. Ten tricks are a certainty at no trumps on any likely lead, and you will therefore need to make eleven tricks in spades to give you a reasonable score.

There are several ways of trying for eleven tricks, but none seems better than a fifty-fifty chance. You could try a finesse of the knave of clubs or the ten of diamonds, or you could just put West on lead by playing a heart to the ten. The trouble with the latter method is that West will probably continue hearts, and a discard from dummy on your knave of hearts will do no good at all.

If West thought you started with only two hearts he would have a real problem, though. Try leading the knave of hearts and crashing dummy's ten. Now West will be unlikely to lead a third heart for fear of giving you a ruff and discard. Instead he will try one of the minor suits, and that will present you with the eleventh trick.

Dummy Play

♠ Q 5
♡ 10 9 7 4
◇ Q 6 4 3   *Game all*
♣ A K 6   *Dealer South*

	South	North
♠ 9 4	1 ♡	3 ♡
♡ A Q J 6 2	4 ♡	—
◇ A		
♣ Q 9 7 4 2		

West leads the knave of diamonds against your four-heart contract. How do you plan the play?

Yes, of course, you should play the queen of diamonds from dummy in order to give yourself the maximum chance of overtricks if the heart finesse is wrong. The deception is well known but there is no reason why it shouldn't work if you follow it up with plenty of guile.

Players rarely lead from interior sequences against suit contracts and it is long odds that East will cover the queen of diamonds with the king. On winning with the ace, you can lead the four of clubs to dummy's ace, so that East may appear to be echoing, and then run the ten of hearts, dropping the six from your hand to give West the chance to miscount the trumps.

If West wins with the king he will have every reason to continue diamonds rather than lead a spade. The fact that your club suit was not mentioned in the bidding will combine with your small deceptions in clubs and hearts to make it appear unlikely that there is any risk of dummy's spades disappearing.

Of course if the heart finesse is right and the hearts and clubs break evenly you will make no fewer than thirteen tricks, but so will everyone else who receives a diamond lead. To gain from your duplicity you must hope for the trump finesse to be wrong.

Defence

In practising deception the defenders are handicapped to some extent by their need to exchange honest information. Defensive false-carding must therefore be limited to the occasions when it cannot hurt if partner is deceived.

There will be times when partner cannot be deceived. When the declarer has shown out of a suit, for instance, both defenders know the position and are ideally placed to indulge in a spot of false-carding designed to give the declarer a distorted picture of the distribution.

There are many well-known situations where it is obligatory for the defenders to play a false card. One example will suffice.

```
              Q 7 3
     10 9 4            K 2
              A J 8 6 5
```

Defence

When the three is led from dummy and the knave finessed, West must drop the nine or ten. Otherwise declarer will have no alternative to the winning play of cashing the ace on the second round.

This routine false-carding is particularly vital in the pairs game. At team or rubber play it assumes major significance only when the setting trick is involved, but at pairs every trick counts and the defenders must not fail to offer the declarer a chance to go wrong.

One of the most powerful weapons in the arsenal of the defence is the hold-up play. This has deceptive as well as technical merits. Defenders who take their aces and kings at an early stage are easy meat for an experienced declarer. With the situation clarified by the release of the defensive stoppers, the declarer is able to make the most of his technical chances on the hand.

It is a very different story if the defenders refuse to part with their stoppers too quickly. After winning a few tricks the declarer will still be uncertain about the location of the outstanding honour cards. If he has to commit himself to a line of play when he is unsure of the lie of the cards he may well go astray.

Ducking is not without its dangers, especially at pairs as many defenders have found out to their cost. We all know the experience of holding up an honour card and later, to our dismay, having to discard it on declarer's string of winners. This sort of thing tends to put the average player off ducking for life.

Most textbooks on play introduce the defensive hold-up at a fairly early stage. It is right to do this, for the learner will never be much good at defence until he has acquired some familiarity with this tool. But it is not generally given sufficient emphasis that the hold-up can be an advanced play. Defenders should not expect to do better than break even with their ducking until they have mastered the arts of card-reading and counting the hand.

More than anything else it is the ability to count that will tell you when you can safely duck and when you must take your ace at once.

Deception

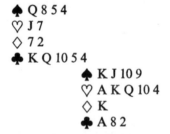

	♠ 3
Game all	♡ 9 8 6 3
Dealer South	◇ A Q J 8 4
	♣ J 9 6

South	North			♠ A 7 6 2
2 ♡	3 ♡			♡ 5 2
4 NT	5 ◇			◇ 10 9 6 5 3
6 ♡				♣ 7 3

Your partner leads the king of clubs and South wins with the ace. Declarer cashes the ace and king of hearts and the king of diamonds, your partner following, and then leads a small heart to dummy's nine, partner throwing a club. On dummy's diamonds the declarer discards two clubs and a spade, while partner throws one of each. Have you made up your mind about what you will do when the spade is led from the table?

The count shows that declarer started with five hearts, one diamond, three clubs and therefore four spades. Since dummy has left only one trump with which to ruff spades there is no danger of the declarer making all thirteen tricks. You should therefore play low on the lead of the three of spades.

	♠ Q 8 5 4
	♡ J 7
	◇ 7 2
	♣ K Q 10 5 4

		♠ K J 10 9
		♡ A K Q 10 4
		◇ K
		♣ A 8 2

If you play low smoothly enough South is likely to take a losing finesse to West's queen, and a spade return will defeat the contract.

When the hand was played in a tournament most players took the ace of spades 'before the rats got at it'. They were not counting.

There are some deceptions peculiar to pairs contests in which the defenders can take advantage of the declarer's greed for extra

Defence

tricks. These usually involve unorthodox play in the suit led in an effort to induce a miscalculation.

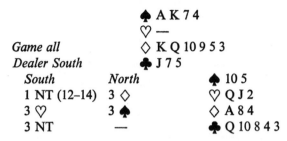

	♠ A K 7 4
	♡ —
Game all	◇ K Q 10 9 5 3
Dealer South	♣ J 7 5

South	North		♠ 10 5
1 NT (12–14)	3 ◇		♡ Q J 2
3 ♡	3 ♠		◇ A 8 4
3 NT	—		♣ Q 10 8 4 3

In spite of the bidding West leads the six of hearts, a club is thrown from dummy, and South plays the three on your knave. How should you continue?

Six diamonds could be on but this does not automatically assure you of a good score. Most North-South pairs will play in no trumps and there may be some who score 620 in five diamonds. Minus 630 could easily be below average for you.

Partner is marked with the king of hearts and declarer with the heart ace and the top clubs. The best way of persuading South to hold himself to nine tricks is to return the two of hearts instead of the normal queen. South may then decide to play safe by holding up his ace three times.

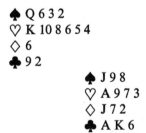

♠ Q 6 3 2
♡ K 10 8 6 5 4
◇ 6
♣ 9 2

♠ J 9 8
♡ A 9 7 3
◇ J 7 2
♣ A K 6

The reverse situation would arise if you had a heart more and a club less. With Q J x x in hearts you should return the queen. Declarer would then be likely to take his ace on the third round, allowing you to beat an unbeatable contract.

Deception

The same theme dominates the next example.

```
            ♠ A 8 3
            ♡ K 6
East-West game   ◇ A J
Dealer South    ♣ Q J 10 7 4 3
  South    North       ♠ K 7
  1 NT (12–14)  3 NT    ♡ Q 10 5 2
                        ◇ 8 6 4 3
                        ♣ A 9 2
```

West leads the queen of spades and the three is played from
dummy. How do you plan the defence?

The bidding marks the declarer with the ace of hearts, the king
and queen of diamonds and the king of clubs, and you are clearly
not going to defeat this contract.

Since partner cannot have an entry there is no point in making
the normal unblocking play in spades. To overtake with the king
and return the seven of spades would, in fact, give the show away.
Declarer would win the second round and attack clubs, finishing
with eleven tricks. Your proper play is the seven of spades on the
first round. When his queen holds the trick partner will continue
the suit and South, placing you with the king and two others,
will allow you to snatch a second spade trick.

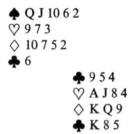

```
            ♠ Q J 10 6 2
            ♡ 9 7 3
            ◇ 10 7 5 2
            ♣ 6
                    ♣ 9 5 4
                    ♡ A J 8 4
                    ◇ K Q 9
                    ♣ K 8 5
```

Conversely, if you held the king and two other spades in the
above situation, the way to extract the maximum number of tricks
would be to 'unblock' by overtaking with the king and returning
a small spade. South might then see no reason to hold up again.

224

Defence

Look at a similar situation from the West seat.

```
          ♠ Q 5
          ♡ K Q J 8
          ◇ A 7 4                Love all
          ♣ K J 10 4           Dealer South
  ♠ 10 6 2                      South    North
  ♡ 9 3 2                       1 NT      2 ♣
  ◇ Q 10 8 5 3                  (12–14)
  ♣ 7 6                         2 ♠       3 NT
```

On your lead of the five of diamonds a low card is played from dummy, partner playing the king and declarer the two. East returns the knave of diamonds and South follows with the six. How should you play?

Partner could have an ace, but the declarer will have just about everything else. If South has the outstanding diamond he will be able to make eleven tricks by taking the ace on the second round.

Clearly it would be wrong to play your three of diamonds for this would present South with a blueprint of the distribution. You could try overtaking partner's knave with your queen, but an astute declarer would probably read you for five diamonds on this play too. The play that gives you the best chance of stealing an extra trick is to follow with the eight of diamonds. If South believes this card he will hold up again, thus limiting himself to ten tricks.

```
          ♠ J 9 7 4
          ♡ 10 7 5
          ◇ K J
          ♣ A 9 5 2
  ♠ A K 8 3
  ♡ A 6 4
  ◇ 9 6 2
  ♣ Q 8 3
```

On the other hand, if you started with only four diamonds and expected partner to have three, you might persuade South to win the second round by overtaking the knave with your queen.

225

Deception

Defenders should bear in mind that declarer is often a worried creature who expects his finesses to fail. Show him how his contract can be made and he may reject a risky play for overtricks.

```
                    ♠ A J 3
                    ♡ A 8 7 4
Game all            ◇ 6
Dealer South        ♣ A Q J 10 4
   South    North                   ♠ 10 8 4
   1 NT (12–14)  3 ♣                 ♡ 9 2
   3 ◇       3 ♡                     ◇ K J 8 5 4 2
   3 ♠       3 NT                    ♣ K 7
```

Partner leads the queen of hearts and dummy plays low. What are your prospects?

There is just room for partner to hold a queen outside the heart suit. If it is the queen of diamonds South will make eleven tricks only, but if partner has the queen of spades South can make a total of twelve tricks by finessing in spades and diamonds. He can only be sure of nine tricks, however, and will be a bit unhappy about taking finesses. You may be able to deflect him from the spade finesse by offering him an easy overtrick elsewhere. Try playing the nine of hearts on the first trick.

When you get in with the king of clubs you can return a diamond to take out an entry. South will have to take that finesse, and when his queen holds he may well go after an eleventh trick in hearts. Partner will split his honours, and although declarer may suspect he has been tricked when you follow suit it will be too late for him to make twelve tricks.

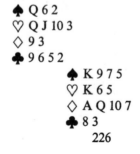

```
        ♠ Q 6 2
        ♡ Q J 10 3
        ◇ 9 3
        ♣ 9 6 5 2
                ♠ K 9 7 5
                ♡ K 6 5
                ◇ A Q 10 7
                ♣ 8 3
```

226

Defence

When the declarer is heading for defeat the defenders can sometimes turn a good score into a superb one by offering him a ray of hope.

```
                    ♠ J 9 7 4
                    ♡ Q 3
                    ♢ J 10 5        North-South game
                    ♣ A K Q 7         Dealer West
      ♠ Q 10 3      West    North    East    South
      ♡ K 9 7 6 2   1 ♡     Double    —      3 NT
      ♢ K Q 4
      ♣ 6           All pass
```

When you try the ace of diamonds partner encourages with the nine. You continue the suit and South discards a club on the third round. On the fourth round of diamonds a heart is thrown from dummy and another club from the South hand. East wins and shoots back the eight of hearts, won by the ace. Declarer then leads out the ace of spades. Have you any ideas?

Yes, of course, you should play the ten of spades in an effort to persuade South to go two down in his contract. If nothing interesting happens on the first round of spades South will settle philosophically for one off by leading a heart at the next trick. But the fall of your ten of spades will leave open for him the possibility of making his contract. The queen and ten doubleton in your hand would allow him to make four spade tricks, one heart and four clubs.

If South continues with the king of spades he will end up a sadder and wiser man, for the defence will then have six tricks.

```
                    ♠ 8 6 2
                    ♡ 8 4
                    ♢ 9 8 6 3
                    ♣ 8 5 4 2
      ♠ A K 5
      ♡ A J 10 5
      ♢ 7 2
      ♣ J 10 9 3
```

227

Deception

Just as the defenders should try to deflect the declarer from a finesse which they know will succeed, so they should offer him every inducement to take a finesse which is wrong.

```
                        ♠ K 5
                        ♡ A Q J
    East-West game      ◇ K J 3
    Dealer North        ♣ A 10 9 5 2
        North    South                  ♠ A Q 7
         1 ♣     1 NT                   ♡ K 9 4
         3 NT     —                     ◇ Q 10 6 5
                                        ♣ 8 7 3
```

Your partner leads the knave of spades against South's three no trump contract. How do you plan the defence?

Most players use the one no trump response over one club to show no four-card suit other than clubs. Partner is therefore likely to have five spades and the contract is going down. If you make this immediately clear to the declarer, he will go only one down, for you can count him for eight tricks in the other suits.

The best plan is to win two spade tricks (declarer will doubtless play the king on the first round, but it doesn't matter) and then switch to the eight of clubs.

Declarer will view your switch as a welcome reprieve and will even entertain hopes of making ten tricks if the heart finesse is right. Even if he is suspicious by nature he is fairly sure to take the heart finesse and thus go two down. After all, he would look silly settling for one down if you really did have only two spades.

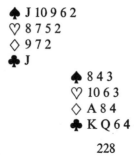

```
    ♠ J 10 9 6 2
    ♡ 8 7 5 2
    ◇ 9 7 2
    ♣ J
                ♠ 8 4 3
                ♡ 10 6 3
                ◇ A 8 4
                ♣ K Q 6 4
```

Defence

Declarers can sometimes be enticed from the straight and narrow path by a judicious false card in the trump suit.

```
                    ♠ 8 3
                    ♡ J 7 4
   Love all         ◇ K 8 4
   Dealer East      ♣ A K Q 10 5
West   North  East    South          ♠ Q J 7 5
              1 ♡     1 ♠            ♡ A K Q 9 2
  —    3 ♣    —       3 ◇            ◇ Q 7 2
  —    3 ♡    —       3 ♠            ♣ 6
```
All pass

Partner leads the ten of hearts and declarer ruffs the third round. South cashes the two top spades, partner following with the two and four. What are your prospects?

Declarer is sure to have the ace of diamonds, and he will now be able to make nine tricks by abandoning trumps and playing on the side suits. That will give you a poor score, for some will play in no trumps where eight tricks are the limit.

The chance of declarer trying for ten tricks by leading a third round of trumps is very slim. Knowing that a 3–3 trump break is against the odds, South will probably make sure of his nine tricks.

You should give him a nudge in the wrong direction by dropping the knave (or the queen) of spades on the second round. Now it will appear safe for him to lead another spade, for a 4–2 break cannot hurt him if the length is with West. If South does play another trump you will be able to force him with your long hearts and put the contract one down.

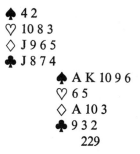

```
        ♠ 4 2
        ♡ 10 8 3
        ◇ J 9 6 5
        ♣ J 8 7 4
              ♠ A K 10 9 6
              ♡ 6 5
              ◇ A 10 3
              ♣ 9 3 2
```

229

Deception

Sometimes the only hope for the defence lies in deceptive discarding on declarer's long suit.

Let us see all four hands for a change.

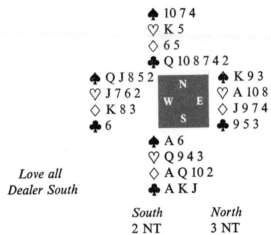

```
                    ♠ 10 7 4
                    ♡ K 5
                    ◇ 6 5
                    ♣ Q 10 8 7 4 2
        ♠ Q J 8 5 2                ♠ K 9 3
        ♡ J 7 6 2      N           ♡ A 10 8
        ◇ K 8 3     W     E        ◇ J 9 7 4
        ♣ 6            S           ♣ 9 5 3
                    ♠ A 6
                    ♡ Q 9 4 3
Love all            ◇ A Q 10 2
Dealer South        ♣ A K J
```

South	North
2 NT	3 NT

You lead the five of spades and partner pleases you by producing the king. Declarer wins the second round of spades and starts on the clubs. How do you choose your discards?

To throw winning spades is unthinkable, and your hearts could prove valuable, so your first two discards should be the three and eight of diamonds. If you may eventually have to bare an honour card it is usually better to do so at an early stage. This is much less dangerous than it appears.

On the fourth club partner will throw the ten of hearts, and this tells you what to do from now on. Your other three discards should be the two, the six and the knave of hearts.

This is quite a plausible sequence of discards. If the declarer believes you have no hearts left he is almost sure to throw you in with a spade lead from dummy in the hope that you will have to lead a diamond up to his ace and queen. South will have to throw hearts on your spades and he will eventually go two down, for partner will retain a heart tenace over dummy's king and five.

Final Analysis

In looking back over what I have written I am conscious that a great deal of space has been devoted to unusual contracts and the various recovery techniques that can be employed. There is a danger of accepting as normal what is abnormal, and at this point I wish to emphasize again that most of the hands you meet in a pairs contest should be bid and played in a perfectly normal manner. It is only about one deal in five that will require special match-point technique.

Overall Strategy

There are two basic approaches to winning pairs strategy, one active and the other passive. The successful player combines these approaches in a blend suitable to the occasion, the opposition, and the state of his score.

The passive approach is by far the more valuable. Players frequently ruin their chances by trying to achieve too much. It is necessary to beat par with fair regularity, but no one should attempt to do so on every hand. Tops cannot be produced at will. Remember that the opponents must slip up before you have a chance of beating par. The correct policy is to wait patiently until an opportunity presents itself. Then be quick to pounce on it.

In adopting the passive approach you will play strictly down the middle, avoiding unusual bids, unusual contracts and unusual plays like the plague. You will not try to be clever and outguess the field, but aim to arrive at the normal contract on hand after

231

hand. In making all your decisions you will try to go with the field, making the bid or play that you think the other players will make.

In this way you hope to achieve a series of average scores. If you succeed in avoiding disasters this will keep the zeros off your score card, and enough presents will inevitably come along to ensure a few tops and pull your score above average.

This passive approach is ideal for a qualifying session, where perhaps one-third of the field will survive and a score of about 55 per cent will guarantee success. It is also the right approach for the start of a long final, or a three-session event with carry-over scores. Play passively until you come to the last session, when you should be in a good striking position.

To win a short single-session final, however, will require a score of 60 per cent or more and you will need to adopt a more active approach. Unless you are very lucky, playing down the middle will not be enough to get your name on the cup. You will have to be a little more venturesome, but this does not mean bidding rashly or playing against the odds. On competitive hands it just means applying a little extra pressure in an attempt to push the opponents overboard, and being a shade quicker on the trigger with your close doubles. In the play of the hand it means taking finely calculated risks for overtricks, and giving the opponents the maximum chance to go wrong. In the uncontested auction you will tend to favour the riskier contract which will bring in the match-points if it succeeds rather than the safe contract some players will choose.

Playing to Your Score

It will often be desirable to vary your approach during the course of a session according to the way the battle is going. Most serious competitors try to estimate their match-point score on each hand as they go along. After a little practice it is possible to achieve a fair degree of accuracy in your estimating, and by the time you are half-way through the session you should have a good idea of where you stand and what you need to achieve in the second half.

In a qualifying session if you are below average at half-time you will probably decide to open up a little and take a few chances in an effort to get back in the running. Similarly, if you have a score of 55 per cent after two sessions of a three-session event, you will need to do a little more in the third session to come out on top.

If, on the other hand, you find yourself sitting on a good lead half-way through a short final, you may well decide to go passive in an attempt to give nothing away in the second half.

Shooting for Tops

In the last stages of a contest it may be clear to you that desperation measures are called for. Perhaps, with six boards to go, you estimate your score to date as 53 per cent. In that case average scores, or even slightly above average, on the next six boards will be of no use to you. You will need tops and practically nothing but tops if you are to finish in your proper place. On such occasions a little judicious shooting may do the trick.

Shooting is a deliberate attempt to achieve an abnormal result. This will usually give you either a top or a bottom score, and it is worth remembering that the bottom is more probable.

The key to successful shooting is to be slightly unorthodox, either in bidding, play or defence. This will often produce a result completely different to those obtained at the other tables. If you are in luck it could mean a top score for you.

Being unorthodox implies going against the odds, but you should take care not to overdo it. Backing a ten to one shot would clearly be foolish, for that would give you ten bottoms for every top you achieve. The trick is to go only slightly against the odds, perhaps backing the second favourite at six to four instead of the favourite at evens.

Some examples will perhaps make this clear.

Final Analysis

Love all
Dealer North

		North	South
♠ K Q 8			1 ♡
♡ J 9 6 3		—	1 ♡
◇ Q J 4		3 ♡	?
♣ A Q 10			

After your partner's limit raise you will not feel too happy about playing in hearts at the four-level with this balanced hand. Partner will have shortage in some suit and there is sure to be duplication present. Nor is three no trumps an attractive proposition. Nevertheless, the field is sure to play in game, and it would normally be folly to do anything but bid on.

This is a good opportunity to shoot for a top by passing your partner's three-heart bid. You can be fairly sure of getting either a top or a bottom, and you must hope for partner to lay down a hand such as:

♠ 6
♡ A K 7 2
◇ 9 7 6 2
♣ K 7 5 4

Nine tricks may well be the limit, in which case your pass will be worth a top.

Note that in shooting you are not trying to beat par. You merely hope for your unorthodox action to achieve par while the normal action misses it.

The shooting technique can be applied to any bidding situation where there is a clearly defined 'normal' action to reject. Here is another case.

♠ 6
♡ A J 7 2
◇ K J 8 4 3
♣ K 4 2

West	North	East	South
		1 ♠	?

Game all. Dealer East

Everyone will double on the above hand because this is the action which will pay on balance. It will not pay every time, of course, and so if you need to shoot this is a good opportunity to

Final Analysis

do so by passing. The doublers might get into trouble on the hand if West has a good redouble. Alternatively, North-South may have the balance of strength and normally reach a game which goes down because of unlucky breaks. Or, after your pass, West could raise to four spades, and without any help from you in the bidding East may misguess the position of the honour cards and go down in a game which other players make.

It is not necessary to look round corners in these situations. There are a dozen different ways in which the pass might earn you a top, although it is naturally rather more likely to give you a bottom.

You've probably heard the story of the pair who decided in advance that they would do nothing but pass throughout on every hand in a tournament. They didn't win, but they finished above average.

An unusual result can be obtained by overbidding just as easily as by passing. When in urgent need of tops you might decide to press on to an odds-against game.

	Game all	
	Dealer North	
	North	*South*
♠ 9 4	1 ♣	1 ♡
♡ K Q 10 9 6 3	1 NT	?
◊ Q 8 5	(15–16)	
♣ 8 6		

Game is unlikely here unless partner has just the right cards or you get a lucky lead. The sensible course of action is to sign off with a bid of two hearts, and this is what most of the other players will do. But if you need to shoot you can take a chance by raising to three no trumps. If North has the ace of hearts you may get away with it.

When you find yourself in the normal contract in spite of everything, the play of the hand may offer the opportunity for shooting that you need.

Final Analysis

```
♠ 10 7 4
♡ A 5
♢ A 9 7 5 3          Game all
♣ K J 8              Dealer South
                     South    North
♠ A K J 9 3          1 ♠      2 ♢
♡ K 9 2              2 ♠      4 ♠
♢ 8 2
♣ Q 10 5
```

Against your four spade contract West leads the queen of hearts, which looks like a standard lead. After ruffing the third heart in dummy, most declarers will give themselves the best chance in finessing against the queen of spades. They will make ten or eleven tricks depending on whether they lose a trump trick or not.

A good opportunity for shooting is available on this hand. By going slightly against the odds and refusing the trump finesse you can be almost sure of getting either a top or bottom.

Any line of play which will not normally be adopted in a pairs contest can be a life-line when you are desperate for tops. Good use can be made, for instance, of the common or garden safety play.

```
♠ 8 4
♡ 7 6
♢ A K Q 8 7 3        Love all
♣ 10 6 2             Dealer South
                     South    North
♠ A J 9 5            1 ♣      1 ♢
♡ A K 4              1 ♠      3 ♢
♢ 6 2                3 NT     —
♣ A 9 7 3
```

Not wishing to be too eccentric, you find yourself in the normal contract of three no trumps. West starts with the queen of hearts which has every appearance of being an automatic lead.

It looks like a flat board anyway, no matter what the lead. The odds are more than two to one in favour of an even diamond

236

Final Analysis

break, and at pairs nobody will consider making a safety play. They will just lead out the diamonds from the top, making ten tricks unless they get a bad break.

If average scores are no use to you this is a splendid opportunity to shoot by ducking the first round of diamonds. This will certainly produce a different result to those obtained at all the other tables. Most likely you will end up with nine tricks while everyone else makes ten. But if your luck is in and the diamonds break 4–1 you will get a top score for making your contract.

♠ J 6 3
♡ 9 4 3
◇ A 8 7 6 3
♣ A J

Game all. Dealer South

	South	West	North	East
	1 NT	All pass		

♠ A Q 7 5
♡ 10 7 6
◇ K Q 4
♣ Q 6 2

On the lead of the five of hearts East takes the ace and continues with the queen and then the two of hearts. West cashes the thirteenth heart and you throw spades from both hands while East discards a club.

West then leads a club and dummy's knave wins. When you test the diamonds they prove to be 3–2. What now?

You have eight certain tricks and two ways of trying for a ninth. The simple method is to take the spade finesse, which is what the field will do. That is normally what you should do too, for you do not want to be out on your own.

If you need tops, however, you should play for West to have both black kings, in which case a criss-cross squeeze will land the ninth trick. Just run the rest of the diamonds, coming down to the bare ace of spades in your hand. West will have to bare one of his kings, and if you read the position correctly you will make the remainder.

There are also plenty of good opportunities for shooting in

237

Final Analysis

defence. The desperation lead of the king from king and another —normally shunned at pairs—begins to look quite attractive when you are hungry for tops. Any play that is at all unusual is likely to produce an unusual result. The underlead of an ace may be all that is needed to hit the jackpot.

```
                        ♠ K Q 7 5
                        ♡ 9
    Game all            ◇ K J
    Dealer South        ♣ A Q 7 6 5 2
South         North                  ♠ J 9 6
1 NT (12–14)  3 ♣                    ♡ A 7 6 3 2
3 ♡           3 ♠                    ◇ A 7 2
3 NT          —                      ♣ 10 8
```

Partner leads the ten of diamonds and you take dummy's knave with your ace.

The sensible, down-the-middle defence is to take the ace of hearts at trick two, for South might be able to make twelve tricks if you do not cash out.

If you need to gamble for a top, however, the lead of a small heart is a fair shot. Partner may have the queen which will give the defence a chance of three tricks.

The opening lead offers you a shooting gallery all of its own.

```
♠ 9 8
♡ A Q 9 6 4        Love all. Dealer South
◇ J 7 2              South      North
♣ 6 5 2              1 NT       3 NT
```

There can be no doubt about the correct lead on this hand at pairs or any other form of the game. The fourth-highest heart stands out, for it will pay handsomely on balance.

Since everyone will be leading the six of hearts, you can shoot by choosing a different lead. The nine of spades will do as well as anything. It may be that declarer has eight tricks on top and a heart lead would present him with the ninth. Alternatively you may hit your partner's entry and get a heart lead back from

Final Analysis

J 10 x to defeat the contract by two tricks. Neither event is particularly likely, but you would have little chance of getting a top by following the herd.

It is important to appreciate that shooting is a complete reversal of the normal winning strategy at pairs. It should therefore be reserved for real emergencies. Even then you will lose out on your shooting most of the time, finishing in a lower position because of it. But occasionally, when everything clicks, you will be able to pull yourself up to a winning score.

Remember, too, that shooting is likely to effect an indiscriminate distribution of tops and bottoms amongst your opponents. In fairness to the other competitors, therefore, shooting should not be indulged in by players who are no longer in the running. There are always enough weird results floating around without anyone adding to them deliberately.

As a last word of advice on pairs strategy, I suggest that the quickest road to an improved performance lies in the cultivation of the passive approach. There is wisdom in the old saying: 'Look after the bottoms and the tops will look after themselves.' If you concentrate on cutting down your errors, the opponents will have little chance of beating par at your expense. It is the self-inflicted zeros that do the real damage to your score and to your morale. Victory in any game usually goes to those who make the fewest mistakes.